The Creation Scriptures

**The Whirlpool Galaxy in the Constellation
Canis Venatici**

Concentrations of glowing matter similar to the Whirlpool Galaxy are scattered in uncounted numbers through the vastness of space. These are called spiral galaxies from the shape suggested by the combination of two curving arms springing from a dense central core or hub.

The Milky Way Galaxy, home of mankind, is known to have a spiral form not unlike millions of others. A typical galaxy contains as many as ten billion stars and great volumes of dust and gas. Energy produced by largely unknown processes pours from the central core to modify surrounding matter. Generations of stars, and perhaps planets, come and go in the dynamic environments of the spiral arms.

Courtesy Mt. Wilson and Palomar Observatories

The Creation Scriptures
A Witness for God in the Scientific Age

William Lee Stokes

INTERNATIONAL STANDARD BOOK NUMBER
0-88290-106-0

LIBRARY OF CONGRESS CATALOG CARD NUMBER
78-71714

Printed in the
United States of America
by

**Horizon Publishers
& Distributors
P.O. Box 490
50 South 500 West
Bountiful, Utah 84010**

available from
Starstone Publishing Company
1354 Second Avenue
Salt Lake City, Utah 84103

Table of Contents

Author's Preface

My hope is that this book will be read by those for whom it was written. It has a special message for those who seek reconciliation between scientific and theological interpretations of the creation scriptures. Reasonable alternatives do exist to replace traditional but impossible explanations of the past. I sincerely hope to reach those who have not made final choices and are not afraid to travel new paths in search of fresh solutions.

In writing and publishing this work I am risking more than time spent in writing it. In the first place I am mixing serious religion with serious science, something that will probably discredit me among my fellow scientists and bring only scorn from theologians. Secondly I am publishing at my own expense and without the imprint of a regular publishing house. Self-publication usually identifies an author who is the victim of his own vanity and a manuscript that no publisher wants to put into print. Finally, I am putting into words many concepts that are at variance with interpretations of respected authorities of the church to which I belong; consequences could be dire. However, I have counted the costs and considered the consequences. I confess my foolhardy actions to assure my readers that my incentives are neither mercenary nor worldly.

It has been my good fortune to have taught the science of the earth (geology) on the university level for 32 years. I have written two widely used texts on the subject. One has been in use for 20 years, the other for seven. My teaching and writing have made me increasingly aware of the need for reasonable reconciliations between science and theology. Had it not been necessary for me to keep up with recent discoveries in astronomy, biology, anthropology and geology I would not have perceived the explanations of the creation scriptures that I describe in this book. Spectacular recent discoveries on earth and in space have opened the way for a new understanding of the creation and of creation scripture.

The intellectual frustrations of past centuries were not due to deficiencies of human reason or impassible barriers to understanding nature. Intricate puzzles cannot be solved when essential pieces are missing. The situation worsens when we try to include pieces that are not parts of the puzzle at all. What we know today has been gained in bits and pieces from many different sources and by the efforts of many individuals. This has taken centuries of time and there have been many false solutions. Now with a much greater number of correct pieces at hand and many wrong ones eliminated we can perceive the broad outlines of what brought the earth into being. I do not mean to assert that we now know or ever can know everything about creation. I do believe we can comprehend the message of the creation scriptures. There is an important distinction here that in itself is part of the puzzle.

Fortunately I have been employed in a free institution where the pursuit of truth is encouraged and where there is time to think things through. My job is not endangered because my employers disagree with me. They might be annoyed or embarrassed but they tolerate new ideas and ways of looking at things. I hope I have not abused my academic privileges. This book has been written entirely on my own time, chiefly in the early morning hours when nothing else interferes.

Perhaps it is also fortunate that my manuscript was rejected by editors and managers of all publishers who deal in L.D.S. books. This has been discouraging but as it now stands any blame or credit that may eventually arise from publication will be exclusively mine. I must state specifically that although the thoughts expressed have their roots and inspiration in latter-day revelation, living authorities of The Church of Jesus Christ of Latter-day Saints have neither approved nor disapproved of my ideas.

I am not seeking friends, favors, or followers. It has been impressed on my mind that it is better to seek truth in its original sources than it is to try to find it is the opinions of others. I intend to apply any profits or contributions resulting from this edition of my book toward publication of another version based exclusively on the biblical version of Genesis. This is intended for those who might be turned away by anything associated with unfamiliar sources. My non-Mormon version is already written and I expect to publish it as soon as I am able. Surely any worthwhile truths about the Bible belong to all people who believe in it.

Throughout my writing the words of Moroni have cheered me:

> For behold, the Spirit of Christ is given to every man, that he may know good from evil, wherefore I show unto you the way to judge, for every thing which inviteth to do good and to persuade to believe in Christ is sent forth by the power and gift of Christ wherefore ye may know with a perfect knowledge that it is of God."
>
> Moroni 7:16

If my book persuades no one to stronger belief in Christ, the Creator, then it has been in vain and should join a long line of ineffective predecessors. The words of God to Isaiah are appropriate. After pointing out the beneficial creations with which he has surrounded his people he gives the reason for their establishment:

"That they may see, and know, and consider, and understand together that the hand of the Lord hath done this, and the Holy One of Israel has created it." (Isaiah 41:20)

Wm. Lee Stokes
October, 1978

The Challenge and Mystery of the Creation Scriptures

The Holy Bible is the world's all-time, best-selling book and has been translated into almost every human language. There must surely be more Bibles in existence than any other written work. Even if most copies have remained unopened and unread the Bible is still the world's most studied book. It is a composite work of many parts not all of which have equal status and value. The Old Testament portion has been in existence much longer and is a part of the sacred writings of far more people than is the New Testament. The first five books of the Old Testament known as the Pentateuch, the Law or the Torah constitute the basis of the Jewish religion. Many other books, written as commentaries and explanations of the laws of Moses have been produced by the Jews.

For several reasons the Book of Genesis is the most studied of the thirty-six writings that make up the Old Testament. Obviously, since Genesis comes first, it has been read by practically all of those whose good intentions were to complete the entire Bible but may have failed at various stages to continue the task. In the second place Genesis has more than its share of the ever-popular, sacred stories that Christians and Jews include in their standard courses of indoctrination and instruction. Finally, it is the basic document of the Creation, a theme considered by most Christians to be second in importance only to the redemptive mission of Jesus Christ.

Quite possibly no written statement in the literature of mankind has been subject to more study than the first two chapters of Genesis. The slightly more than 1,400 words making up the 56 arbitrary verses in the King James Version and their equivalent in other versions and translations have been scanned by countless millions of casual readers in search of nothing more than their Sunday School gold stars, perused deeply by countless devout believers searching for solace and assurance, dissected by hundreds of scholars looking for new or hidden meanings and combed over by infidels and enemies of religion for reasons helpful to their various causes.

It is worth emphasizing that scripture-reading is one of the most time-honored pursuits of literate men. Dating as it does from the time of Moses the Book of Genesis has been available in one form or another for over three thousand years. There is good evidence that many had access to it even in ancient times. The writer of Ecclesiastes was led to exclaim long before Christ: "Of the making of many books there is no end." Among the many books of ancient times the works of Moses must have had a prominent place.

The Genesis account is not the only explanation of how things came into being. Myths and legends of creation are part of the folklore of every culture. That most of these stories are products of human imagination is perfectly clear. The Biblical account is not so easily disposed of; its brevity, dignity, simplicity, and comprehensiveness place it in a class by itself. Topics treated in the creation scriptures are fundamental and have been debated for centuries not only by those who accept the Bible as holy writ but also by those who may never have heard of Hebrew scriptures as such.

The problem of origin runs like a varicolored thread through history, science, philosophy and religion. The poet Vergil said: Happy is he who knows the origin of things. No science is fully understandable without its historical perspective. The Book of Genesis, telling of the origin of heaven and earth and all that in them is, stands at the very fountain-head of the Christian and Jewish faiths. The most influential non-theological book ever written is said to be the *Origin of Species* by Charles Darwin. And practically every research scientist has written at least one paper beginning "The Origin of _____."

The history of the search for beginnings is so vast that only a few key personalities and important chronological developments can be mentioned here.

Classical Philosophers: Socrates, Plato and Aristotle are regarded as the greatest thinkers of ancient time. Together with others such as Anaximander, Empedocles, Democritus, and Hippocrates they are known as the natural philosophers. They sought a coherent, natural explanation of things. Socrates and Plato emphasized methods of arriving at the truth in connection with ethical and political matters. Aristotle, by contrast, became intensely involved with nature, particularly with living things. He and his numerous assistants amassed vast collections and he wrote over 100 treatises on almost every phase of human knowledge.

Aristotle believed in a single God but his supreme being was remote and impersonal, served mainly as a philosophical necessity and had little to do with human affairs. Aristotle taught the eternity of the world but did not speculate extensively on the connection of God and the creation. By comparison with his biologic contributions Aristotle's writings on cosmology and earth science are relatively limited and mostly erroneous. Aristotle's works were so highly prized that they were preserved, copied and translated with unusual care. They became the basic documents of science for 1,800 years and naturally had a powerful influence on Christian thinkers who tried to adjust their understanding of scripture to the learning of the world.

Early Explanations of the Mosaic Account: The Greek philosophers were not interested in what the Hebrew scriptures had to say about the origin of things. Not much is preserved of early writings either for or against the Mosaic account and those which are known lack the sophistication and learning that were to come later. One of the earliest defenders of the creation scripture was Philo of Alexandria, born about 20 B.C. His works *On the Creation of the World* and *Allegories of the Sacred Laws,* were written from the Jewish viewpoint, and are based on the premise that the first two chapters of Genesis are allegorical and their words, phrases and images convey chiefly fundamental philosophical truths. That literal meanings could not possibly be intended is illustrated by Philo's comments about the six creative "days."

> "It would be a sign of great simplicity to think that the world was created in six days, or indeed at all in time; because all time is only the space of days and nights, and these things the motion of the sun as he passes over the earth and under the earth does necessarily make. But the sun is a portion of heaven, so that one must confess that time is a thing posterior to the world. Therefore it would be correctly said that the world was not created in time, but that time had its existence in consequence of the world. For it is the motion of the heaven that has displayed the nature of time." (*The Essential Philo,* Nahum N. Glatzer Ed., Schocken Books, p. 42-43, 1971.)

Philo went on to explain that the creation was not really accomplished in six literal days. The significance lies in the number six being the first perfect number. That is, it is equal to the sum of its factors, the half (3), the third (2), and the sixth parts (1) being the same quantity as that produced by multiplying the two unequal factors 2 and 3. That is: $1 \times 2 \times 3 = 1$ plus 2 plus $3 = 6$. Philo seems to have believed that all the numbers found in Genesis had hidden allegorical meanings.

Early Christian Explanations: In their contact with competing religions and philosophies many early Christian as well as Jewish thinkers found it necessary to explain the six-day creation. As a matter of fact a class of writings defending Genesis called the Hexameral Treatises appeared in the fourth century. Arguments based on firsthand knowledge of Christ or his immediate successors gradually lost influence and later writers followed the pattern of the philosophical and mystical thinkers of the outside world. Thus symbolic and figurative meanings were searched for and adjustments were made with prevailing knowledge of the natural world.

Origen, a Christian Father of the third century A.D., answered the claims of his contemporary anti-Christian critics that Genesis contains elements impossible to believe.

"Suppose someone were to assert that there never was any Trojan War because of the impossible story interwoven (with the *Illiad* account of the War) about a certain Achilles being the son of a sea-goddess Thetis and a human Peleus.... Bearing in mind the weight of fictions which have become attached to it (I know not how), how should we prove that it had in fact occurred, and that—as everyone believes—there was really a war at Illium between Greeks and Trojans?" (Quoted in *The Discovery of Time,* Stephen Toulmin and June Goldfield, Harper Torchbooks, 1965, p. 59.)

How much stronger Origen's argument is today after the excavation and authentication of Troy in the nineteenth century! Origen was on a path that was to become a well-traveled road taken by all those who believe they can pick and choose among the elements of Genesis according to whether these elements appear to be literal or not.

The roots of all subsequent approaches to understanding the creation scriptures may be found in early Christian writings. There were concordists attempting to establish as much conformity of scripture with science as possible, also literalists, believing in word for word scriptural truth, and advocates of allegorical, figurative and symbolical meanings. As to the origin of the creation scriptures as such, some maintained that they were borrowed from ancient pre-Hebrew sources, some thought they were independent Hebrew developments, some that they combine Hebrew forklore and Divine revelation and finally many remained convinced of an entirely Divine origin.

St. Augustine (354-430): St. Augustine was a Christian philosopher and the greatest of the Fathers. He contributed probably more to theological thought and literature than anyone else in the first millennium of the Christian era. He was much concerned with the proof of God's reality and drew his arguments from human reason and experience. He acknowledged the testimony of created things and held the view, in common with other early Christian writers, that God created the world out of nothing. He believed also that the soul of man is created by God but was not specific as to the time and place of its origin. He leaned heavily on Aristotle in matters concerning the natural world and was even more limited by a lack of reliable scientific information.

The Roman Empire and Church of Rome: Christ was born when Rome ruled the world and was crucified within the jurisdiction of Roman Law. It is one of the great ironies of history that the Christian religion, at first a minor irritant, grew to become a major threat and later the state religion. It was within the framework of Roman rule that the confrontation between Judaeo-Christian religion and Greek philosophy took place and the Romans were not particularly interested in the success of either faction. The Romans were tolerant in many ways but were continually battling against instrusive religious influences and were particularly harsh on Christians. The details of secular history are well authenticated but the stern repression of religion during the early centuries of the Christian Era resulted in loss of documents and many historical gaps.

Rome eventually collapsed and although the Church of Rome attempted to carry on a unifying influence there were centuries of disorder and unrest before political stability was again established. It is difficult and unnecessary to trace the history of the intricate struggles for political power and ecclestical dominance that went on during this period.

From about 500 to 1000 A.D. was a time known as the Dark Ages during which men had little time for anything but the struggle to survive. Most Europeans could neither read nor write and scholarship was confined chiefly to the monasteries. Insofar as scriptures are concerned the picture of a monkish scribe laboriously copying a valued manuscript by hand with little critical understanding of the meaning of the words he traced perhaps conveys the spirit of the time better than anything else that might be imagined.

Arabic Influences: In 635 A.D. the Arabs began a lightning-swift conquest that extended their empire across the known world from Spain to India. They carried an unbending belief in the Koran which has much in common with the Bible and teaches a six-day creation by an all-powerful God. While Europe was in the Dark Ages Arab scholars made important advances in learning. They were largely responsible for preserving the works of Aristotle and for transmitting these to western thinkers later on. Islam (the name by which Mohammedans know their religion) does not seem to have been shaken by a confrontation with science such as came to the Christian world. This is possibly because alternate interpretations of the Koran and arguments about its meaning are not officially permitted.

Judiasm: Judiasm and Christianity have much in common. To most historians Christianity is seen as an offspring of Judiasm. To Latter-day Saints Judiasm is an aberration of Christianity. In any event the first five books of the Old Testament, or the Torah of the Jews is held in highest regard by both groups and the problem of explaining and defending creation scripture falls on both Jew and Christian. A recent exposition on the philosophy of Judiasm states that, "It is a primary ordinance of faith that the world came into being *creatio ex nihilo,* substance from void" (Joshua Adler, *Philosophy of Judiasm,* Philosophical Library, 1960). All phenomena of time, space, generation, and degeneration were created and not eternally present. Jews have had the same troubles adjusting to science that Christians have had.

St. Thomas: Thomas Aquinas (1225-1274), usually referred to as St. Thomas, was a profound Catholic thinker and writer. He is called by some the Aristotle of the West. His influence on both Catholic and Protestant thinking has been incalculable and lasting. It is generally conceded that his great contribution was a more or less successful reconciliation of the philosophy of Aristotle with Christian theology. Rather than accept Aristotle outright, St. Thomas rethought him very thoroughly and his philosophical system is accepted by Catholics as a standard against which dissention must not be evidenced without compelling reasons. St. Thomas taught that God created the world out of nothing. On this point he is at variance with Aristotle who clearly teaches that the world is eternal and not created by God.

St. Thomas cannot be described as particularly strict in his interpretation of scripture. For instance he wrote on this subject:

> "Concerning the second way of considering this question, there are also two errors to be avoided. The first point is that no one should say that something patently false is to be understood in the texts of Scripture that deal with the creation of things. Indeed, falsity cannot form the basis of divine Scripture which has been handed down by the Holy Spirit; nor can there be falsity in the faith that is taught therein. The other point to be avoided is that no

one should try to restrict Scripture to one meaning, to such an extent that other meanings, containing some truth and quite possible in relation to the context, would be excluded. In fact, it belongs to the dignity of divine Scripture to contain many meanings in one text, so that in this way it may be appropriate to the various understandings of men for each man to marvel at the fact that he can find the truth that he has conceived in his own mind expressed in divine Scripture. Also, this makes it more easily defended against nonbelievers; for, if something that a person wants to understand in Sacred Scripture appears false, then he may be referred to an alternative meaning.

Consequently, it is not unbelievable that Moses and the other writers of Sacred Scripture were divinely inspired so that they would know the different true meanings that men would be able to find, and so that they could express them in one textual form, in such a way that each of them is the author's meaning. Hence, even if some truths that the writer did not have in mind are associated with the text of Sacred Scripture by commentators, there is no doubt that the Holy Spirit understood them, for He is the principal Author of divine Scripture. Thus, every truth that can be fittingly related to divine Scripture, in view of the context, is its meaning."

Revival of Learning: As the western world emerged from the Dark Ages science began to assume ever-increasing importance. Observation and experiment took the place of scriptural analysis and appeal to long-dead authorities such as Aristotle. The telescope was improved and the microscope invented. Voyages of discovery and exploration brought back new knowledge and specimens from distant places. Universities were established with expanded courses of study. The digging of canals, opening of mines, and building of roads brought increasing contact with the earth and its products including fossils. The life, contributions, and controversies of Leonardo da Vinci (1452-1591) illustrate in one personality much of the spirit of the time. The exercise of his many talents and the necessity of earning a living brought him into an uneasy alliance with both ecclesiastical and political institutions at all levels. In his secret records (he wrote backwards in Latin script and many of his journals were not interpreted until the nineteenth century) he revealed an independence of thought and spirit that was to blossom in later centuries. Leonardo was self-taught and thus did not become infected with the devious thinking habits of the formally trained scholars of his time. He wrote:

"A lie is so vile, that even if it spoke well of divine things, it would detract from their charm; truth is of such excellence that it lends nobility to the meanest things that it praises. Truth, even if it has to do with insignificant and inferior things, is infinitely superior to uncertain opinions concerning the most sublime and exalted problems.... But you who live in dreams, you find your pleasure in the sophisms concerning revealed uncertain things rather than in certain, natural conclusions that do not rise to such heights."

The Copernican Revolution and Trial of Galileo: Volumes of history must be passed over if we are to avoid becoming diverted too far from the subject at hand. It was in the life of Galileo Galilei (1566-1642) that the inevitable conflict of science and theology came to a climax. Galileo's trial on charges of heresy took place in 1633. Much has been written about this episode. A good account is that of Arthur Koestler, *The Sleepwalkers,* Grosset and Dunlap, 1959. For lack of space we quote only a passage or two of the pertinent documents. The introduction of formal charges brought against Galileo by the Inquisition reads:

"Whereas you, Galileo, son of the late Vincenzo Galilei, Florentine, aged seventy years, were in the year 1615 denounced to this Holy Office for holding as true the false doctrine taught by some that the Sun is the centre of the world and immovable and that the Earth moves, and also with a diurnal motion; for having disciples to whom you taught the same doctrine; for holding correspondence with certain mathematicians of Germany concerning the same; for having printed certain letters, entitled "On the Sunspots," wherein you developed the same doctrine as true; and for replying to the objections from the Holy Scriptures, which from time to time were urged against it, by glossing the said Scriptures, according to your own meaning: and whereas there was thereupon produced the copy of a document in the form of a letter, purporting to be written by you to one formerly your disciple, and in this divers propositions are set forth, following the position of Copernicus, which are contrary to the true sense and authority of Holy Scripture:"

The same document records the fateful assertions of Galileo's persecutors that:

"The Proposition that the Sun is the centre of the world and does not move from its place is absurd and false philosophically and formally heretical, because it is expressly contrary to the Holy Scripture.

The Proposition that the Earth is not the centre of the world and immovable but that it moves, and also with a diurnal motion, is equally absurd and false philosophically and theologically considered at least erroneous in faith."

The record proves that Galileo did "abjure, curse, and detest the aforesaid errors and heresies" and swore never again to repeat them. He spent his last years, an old man in his seventies, in virtual confinement in his own house.

The so-called Copernican Revolution went in favor of science and to the detriment of organized religion. While foes of religion might judge that the Bible became a disreputable document as a result of these early encounters it is clear that the blame is with faulty interpretation and human error and not with the scriptures as such.

It is unfortunate that Aristotle had erroneous ideas about the structure of the cosmos and that these remained unchallenged for so long. He taught that the earth is at the center of things and it is surrounded by transparent spheres. These teachings were accepted by almost everyone during the Middle Ages and had to be combatted by better informed thinkers such as Copernicus and Galileo. As a matter of fact Galileo was more in conflict with Aristotle than he was with the Church.

For better or worse the grip of organized religion was loosened. The protestant movement weakened the power of the universal church but it both helped and hindered the advancement of science. The primacy and authority of the scriptures were asserted by Calvin and Luther and there was a return to literal interpretations that, insofar as natural sciences are concerned, were little better than those of the early middle ages. Luther referred to Copernicus as "a fool who went against Holy Writ."

From Galileo to Darwin: The interval between the birth of Galileo Galilei in 1564 and the death of Charles Darwin in 1882 is marked by many serious but generally futile attempts to reconcile scripture and the growing body of scientific facts and theories. Not only theologians but scientists were optimistic that geology and biology would verify Genesis. Education at that time was such that well-informed persons were versed in both theology and science. Many scientists who were prominent in the early development of chemistry, physics, zoology, botany and geology were devout Christians.

The Reverend John Ray (1627-1705), pioneer botanist, declared that the "...Works created by God at first, and by Him conserved to this Day in the same State and Condition in which they were first made." Linneaus (1707-1778) who knew more plants and animals than anyone else of his time was convinced "...that of all the species originally formed by Diety not one is destroyed."

Isaac Newton (1642-1727), considered by many to be the greatest scientist who ever lived, was deeply religious and wrote extensively on theological subjects. Among early geological observers none ranks higher than Nicholas Steno (1638-1686). His writings reveal a fundamental understanding of superposition and the meaning of fossils. Steno's chief interests were in theology, however, and he became a Catholic Bishop and spent most of his life carrying out the duties of this office. Another important figure of unusually wide attainments was the Frenchman, Georges Couvier (1769-1832), father of vertebrate paleontology. With great brilliance he defended the idea that fossils were formed by Noah's Flood and other catastrophies. He also sternly opposed the idea of organic evolution. A pioneer American geologist was James D. Dana (1813-1895). The closing words of his popular *Textbook of Geology* (2nd Ed. 1874) are these:

> "Man may well feel exalted to find that he was the final purpose when the word went forth in the beginning, Let there be light. And he may thence derive direct personal assurance that all this magnificent preparation is yet to have a higher fulfillment in a future of spiritual life. This assurance from nature may seem feeble, yet it is at least sufficient to strengthen faith in that Book of books in which the promise of that life and "the way" are plainly set forth." (p. 345)

This very incomplete list indicates that there was a time when many leading scientists were convinced that their findings could be reconciled with Christian scriptures. Many readily admitted supernatural influences in their respective fields to explain what appeared to be unexplainable by natural means. But, one by one, these theological arguments were weakened and discredited. The ranks of agnostics expanded. Charles Darwin had the good sense to avoid theological arguments but he clearly rejected the scriptures as being valuable in interpreting nature. Outright atheists, such as Thomas H. Huxley appeared and voiced compelling arguments against traditional theology.

The Restoration: In 1820 Joseph Smith (1805-1844), latter-day American prophet received the first vision that opened the dispensation of the fullness of time. In this and subsequent revelations he was taught and learned answers to questions that are basic to theology, science, and philosophy. That the topic of creation is of more than usual importance in this restoration of knowledge is shown by the fact that two accounts of creation, the Book of Moses and the Book of Abraham, were brought forth at an early date. In addition to these supplements to Genesis other important concepts bearing on God and the creation are scattered throughout the inspired writings of the Prophet.

Among the truths revealed in latter-day scriptures are these: 1) There is a God and he is an exalted man, 2) There is a plurality of Gods, 3) A number of gods took part in the creation, 4) Matter is eternal, 5) Creation consisted of the organization of pre-existant matter in pre-existant space, 6) There was a "spiritual creation" in which all living things had a potential beginning or being before they were "naturally" upon the earth, 7) Man is eternal and is a personage of physical body and divinely organized spirit. "The spirit and the body are the soul of man," 8) There are many worlds, they are continually being organized and annihilated by God, 9) These other worlds are also inhabited by offspring of God presumably not unlike mankind on earth.

The Darwinian Revolution: Thinking citizens of the western world had scarcely recovered from the rude shock of having their earth degraded to a mere speck in an inconceivably vast universe when another threat appeared. Now the very nature and status of man himself was under attack. The banner of this dangerous foe reads organic evolution.

The thought that there had been a progressive change in living things is an old one but the task of putting it in unmistakable terms fell to Charles Darwin (1809-1882). His book, *On the Origin of Species by Means of Natural Selection or the Preservation of Favored Races in the Struggle for Life,* is one of the most influential every written and one that has stirred a conflict that still endures.

Unfortunately the idea of organic evolution has been translated by the person on the street as "man from monkey" a concept that is inaccurate, unjust, and unnessarily provocative.

Civilization had at least advanced to the point where a man like Darwin would not be brought to a formal trial as a heretic. Nevertheless, he has suffered a stream of abuse and criticism from theological writers that can scarcely be matched in history. Darwin came to court after his death in a very real sense in Dayton, Tennessee, U.S.A., July, 1925. Here took place the trial of John Thomas Scopes, sometimes called the "monkey trial," one of the most famous cases ever debated before a jury. Scopes was charged with violating a state law which prohibited the teaching of evolution. Two great Americans of the age faced each other in the courtroom, William Jennings Bryan, the Great Commoner, and Clarence Darrow, brilliant, liberal, agnostic criminal lawyer. When Darrow questioned Bryan, it was chiefly on biblical subjects. Topics included Jonah and the whale, Joshua and the standing still of the sun, Noah's Flood, the contents of the Ark, the rainbow, the beginnings of religion and civilization, the Garden of Eden and the date of the Creation. Bryan proved to be a difficult witness and evaded most of Darrow's questions. However, his attempted defense of literal scripture proved his undoing. The following exchange, essentially as reported in the court records, illustrates this:

> *Darrow:* "Then, when the Bible said, for instance 'and God called the firmament Heaven. And the evening and the morning were the second day' that does not necessarily mean twenty-four hours?"
>
> *Bryan:* "I do not think it necessarily does."
>
> *Darrow:* "Do you think it does or does not?"
>
> *Bryan:* "I know a great many think so."
>
> *Darrow:* "What do you think?"
>
> *Bryan:* "I do not think it does."
>
> *Darrow:* "You think these were not literal days?"
>
> *Bryan:* "I do not think they were twenty-four-hour days."
>
> *Darrow:* "What do you think about it?"

(After a few more extraneous remarks the line of questioning continued.)

> *Bryan:* "My impression is that they were periods, but I would not attempt to argue as against anybody who wanted to believe in literal days."

Darrow: "Have you any idea of the length of the periods?"

(More verbal exchanges as Darrow tried to get a precise statement from Bryan.)

Darrow: "...Now, if you call these periods, they may have been a very long time?"

Bryan: "They might have been."

Darrow: "The Creation might have been going on for a very long time?"

Bryan: "It might have continued for millions of years."

This was devastating to those who expected Bryan to give a better defense of Genesis. There must be another lesson here for all who would attempt a literal interpretation of every word and phrase of scripture. Some say Bryan lost the battle, as a matter of fact he died only 5 days after the conclusion of the trial. Some say Darrow lost for he failed to see biology textbooks include the topic of evolution in a straightforward manner.

Several things seem clear—neither Darrow nor Bryan understood the Bible, for not even in fact and historical matters were they correct. In the heat of debate and anger they said things that they may have regretted. They didn't change each other's minds and probably no one there changed his or hers either.

Expansion of Science and Retreat of Theology: Starting roughly with the publication of the *Origin of Species* the western world entered a period dominated by science and technology. Knowledge accumulated at an accelerated rate to provide subject matter for ever-increasing specialized fields. There was a time when theology covered everything. Philosophy as a separate discipline split from theology early in the middle ages. Science and metaphysics arose from philosophy. Science divided into social and physical science. Distinctions then arose within physical science to produce astronomy, chemistry, physics, biology and geology. Social science became anthropology, sociology, economics and psychology. There are now numerous hybrid fields such as biophysics and astrophysics and geophysics, also biochemistry, astrochemistry and geochemistry.

Where once the pride of a superior mind was to comprehend all knowledge the goal has shifted to specialization in a small neat compartment of it. The cynical remark that the specialist knows more and more about less and less until he knows everything about nothing while the generalist knows less and less about more and more until he knows nothing about everything is more than just a clever play on words. Ironically, theology, the mother of sciences, is seldom thought of as a science today—a fact one may verify by looking at any selection of college catalogs.

As though by some inverse process the power of religion declined as that of science increased. Within the last few decades science appears to have greatly weakened and perhaps nearly demolished the traditional interpretations of Genesis. Bryan would have a tougher time today than in 1925. Biblical scholars seem to be the first to admit this. The entry on Genesis is that prestigious compendium of human knowledge, the Encyclopaedia Britannica (1952 Ed.), reports: "That the records of the prehistoric ages in Genesis I-XI are at complete variance with modern science and archaeological research is unquestionable." Similar statements can be found in the writings of modern scholars in most Christian churches. A few may be quoted: "...the bible has nothing to say about the physical process by which man was created, or about the time it may have taken, just as it has nothing to say about the vast ages in which the universe was in formation," (*The Lessons of Genesis,* Catholic Information Service, Knights of Columbus, 1964, p. 10-11.); "...The Bible gives us no answers to scientific questions; its authors had no access to supernatural sources of information about scientific problems such as the age of the earth...," (Alan Richardson, *The Bible in the Age of Science,* SMC Press Ltd. 1961, p. 166-167); "...the inspired writers of the Bible do not and cannot attempt to give a scientific account of origins," (Raymond J. Nogar, *The Wisdom of Evolution,* New American Library, 1966, p. 296); "This chapter (Genesis) is no scientific treatise. Labored effort to make it appear that its picture of creation does parallel here and there the conclusions of modern science is misconceived and misdirected," (*Interpreters Bible,* vol. 1, p. 469); "It is clear at the outset, that it is impossible to maintain the Biblical stories of creation in their literal sense," (*Universal Jewish Encyclopedia,* vol. 3, 1941, p. 398); "It gradually became clear that the inspired writer, expressing himself in the accepted literary forms of his day, had no intention of giving a scientific description...," (*The New Catholic Encyclopedia,* 1967, p. 424); "God's act of creation is incomprehensible to our reason," (*The Encyclopedia of the Lutheran Church,* 1965, p. 621).

The Anti-science Revolt: Although fewer and fewer scientists in proportion to total numbers are inclined to place literal interpretations on the creation scriptures there are notable exceptions. An organized resurgence of support for traditional Christian interpretations of the Bible has emerged among scientists in the form of the

Creation Research Society. According to a statement in the official *Creation Research Society Quarterly* the organization is composed of research scientists committed to full belief in the Biblical record of creation and early history. The Society is strongly opposed to evolution—"All basic types of living things, including man, were made by direct creative acts of God during the Creation Week described in Genesis." Members avow belief in the great Flood as a historic event "...worldwide in its extent and effect." The eventual goal is the "realignment of science based on theistic concepts...."

Another organization, the Institute for Creation Research (ICR) is actively engaged in spreading creationist literature. The organization is working "...to bring about a revival of belief in special creation as the true explanation of the origin of the world." The research, literature, and education programs of ICR are bible-based. A list of some of the books put out by the Institute illustrates the areas in which conventional science is being opposed: *Origins: Two Models, Biology: A Search for Order in Complexity, Evolution? The Fossils Say NO!, The Genesis Flood, Scientific Creationism, The Genesis Record, The Ark on Ararat, Why Not Creation,* and *Many Infallible Proofs.*

The anti-science movement is widespread. The Creation Research Society and Institute for Creation Research represent but a small vocal segment of a much larger group that is unnumbered, unorganized and difficult to define. These are significant clues to what is happening. In 1976 a Gallup poll revealed that four out of ten U.S. citizens believe that the Bible "is to be taken literally, word for word." This should bring sobering thoughts to science teachers and those doing research in fields that are considered unfriendly to traditional biblical interpretations.

Summary and Conclusions

The Holy Bible is the greatest source of spiritual truth and inspiration in the possession of man. It has been accepted as the revealed word of God by countless millions both in and out of the organized Judeo-Christian religious sects. It affirms the creative role of God in the bringing forth of all things and gives reason for the uniqueness of man. However, the Bible is not man's only witness; the natural world also inspires belief in a Supreme Being. The findings of science, in the mind of the average man, constitute compelling evidence of a benevolent creator. Two lines of evidence for the same thing should be stronger than one and together they should be invincible. Ironically this has not proven to be the case. Instead of bringing harmony among religious men and widespread reverence for God there has resulted an age-long controversy generally known as the conflict between science and theology.

The history of attempted reconciliation between the scriptural account of creation and the findings of science has been a painful story of intellectual frustration. The desire to believe in both sources of evidence has been hampered by both scriptural and scientific interpretations that appear to be hopelessly illogical, impossible and contradictory. Plainly the Supreme Being, whose awe-inspiring works are manifest in nature, cannot be, in the minds of most men, the God of Genesis and certainly not Jesus Christ of the New Testament who calls sinful men to repentence and all to moral responsibility. The God-of-Nature and God-of-the-Bible remain unreconciled and apart.

The average thinking person who sincerely wishes to believe in a supreme being is trapped between two seemingly infallible sources of truth, scientific fact and divine revelation. The spokesmen for each side seem well-informed and unshakable in their beliefs. How can the common man question either side and how can he choose between them?

Many have obviously sided with science as the destined winner. This includes not only most scientists but also many theologians. Even the most zealous fundamentalists have had to bend here and there as Bryan did at the Scopes trial. Science is taught with power and authority at all educational levels and the programs and projects of scientists are blessed with vast sums from the public treasury. The past performance of science seems to justify this admiration and support. The wonders and triumphs of science pour forth daily to become the common knowledge of every man. The products of science and technology have passed the stage of being niceties and luxuries, they are now absolute necessities without which civilization could not exist.

Contrary to what one might believe from current events the victory of science is not complete. Just as religion seems to have spawned anti-religion so science may be giving rise to anti-science. Under the surface powerful counter currents are gathering force. Modern civilized man, faced with restrictions and shortages can visualize dark days ahead and he can find reason to criticize science as being in part responsible. There is less confidence now that greater technical knowledge is capable of bringing happiness to the individual or of saving the race from a miserable doom. It is not surprising that the present is a time of religious revival. That 90 percent of Americans should declare faith in God and four out of ten of them believe that the Bible is literal word for word truth has implications that religion, far from being dead, is alive and growing. But it is not the traditional old-line organized churches that are recovering from their long decline, rather it is the newer evangelical and fundamentalist sects that are showing the greatest vitality.

The new religious stirrings are definitely Bible-oriented. Popular evangelists who appear regularly on radio and television do their preaching with scriptures in hand and the so-called Bible Belt is where their cause prospers. Possibly more people are reading and believing the Bible than ever before.

The present religious situation is difficult to explain or describe. The ancient issues that stirred intellectual turmoil in the past have not been resolved and are, if anything, more pressing than ever. The problems of the existence or non-existence of God and the veractiy of the Holy Bible can scarcely be described as trivial. In the past the common people left the solution of these problems up to their religious and secular leaders, now they seek to know for themselves on a personal basis. An amazing 34 percent of those questioned in a recent (1976) Gallup poll claim to have had a personal "born again" experience when they committed themselves to Jesus Christ.

What then has become of the science-theology controversy? It has not simply gone away—the basic problem of interpreting the creation scriptures remain unsolved and two opposing forces under the banners of Creationism and Evolutionism clearly exist. Nevertheless, active combat seems to be at a low ebb. Confrontations have been minor since the battle of the Scopes trial. Results seem invariably the same, science wins with a multitude of facts, theology loses with too many outmoded and unreasonable interpretations.

Even though Creationists will not admit defeat and scientists appear to have lost interest in fighting, nothing has really been ꜱttled. What prevails is a state of wary avoidance, weary apathy and non-communication. An uneasy truce prevails as science refrains from trying to convince theology of its errors and theology leaves science to go its misguided Godless way. The need for reconciliation is greater than ever. The split between science and theology that has widened since the time of Galileo must be counted as a major historical tragedy. It sent the heart and mind in different directions and robbed man of the unity he needs to attain the happier existence to which he is entitled. But reconciliation appears to be impossible. The experience of those who attempted it in the 17th and 18th centuries has discouraged almost all theologians and scientists from further efforts. Perhaps the middle road is not closed. It is well to remember that earlier thinkers who traversed it had but a small fraction of the information that exists today. Perhaps instead of making reconciliation more difficult new knowledge has eased the way. Certainly the cure for error and misunderstanding is more truth—and we have more truth than ever before.

The time has come for science to demonstrate that it seeks for and builds on promising hypotheses and pursues truth wherever it leads. Likewise theology must be willing to prove that it too holds truth in highest regard and is the enemy of error wherever it is found. But there can be no understanding, no reconciliation and no vindication of truth without some very fundamental changes of attitude. It is a reproach to man's intelligence and wisdom that a deep schism exists between his intellectual and spiritual experience. The challenge of the times is to heal this division with any and all remedies at our command.

> "Upon this gifted age, in its dark hour,
> Rains from the sky a meteoric shower
> Of facts...they lie unquestioned,
>   uncombined.
> Wisdom enough to leech us of our ill
> Is daily spun; but there exists no loom
> To weave it into fabric..."
>
> Edna St. Vincent Millay
> Collected Sonnets

Comments and References

The scope of human history is so vast that few minds can comprehend more than small segments of it. Mostly history is studied in bits and pieces restricted to certain time spans, peoples, or political entities. Comprehensive surveys include the time-honored *Outline of History* by H. G. Wells; *The Story of Mankind* by Hendrick W. Van Loon, and the epoch marking 11-volume, *The Story of Civilization* by Will and Ariel Durant. These summaries are sufficient to substantiate the major points of this chapter. More about individual personalities and events as, for instance, Aristotle or the Dark Ages, can be found in specific books or articles. As a general rule, standard encyclopedias such as the Encyclopaedia Britannica and Encyclopaedia Americana carry concise, unbiased, and scholarly articles on all significant aspects of history. There are also a number of encyclopaedias that cover human knowledge from narrower denominational viewpoints; these are found only in larger libraries.

Books dealing with the growth of scientific ideas about the universe are Alexander Koyre, 1957, *From the Closed World to the Infinite Universe,* John Hopkins; Arthur Koestler, 1963, *The Sleepwalkers,* Grosset and Dunlap; W. C. Dampier, 1966, *A History of Science and its Relations with Philosophy and Religion,* Cambridge; C. A. Coulson, 1958, *Science and Christian Belief,* Collins; George Sarton, 1970, *A History of Science,* Harvard University Press; and Sir Alan Cottrell, 1977, *Portrait of Nature: the World as Seen by Modern Science,* Scribners.

An account of the gradual decline of theological influences on students of natural science is John C. Greene, 1959, *The Death of Adam,* Mentor Books. Dealing more specifically with geological controversies is C. C. Gillispie, 1959, *Genesis and Geology,* Harper and Row. The subtitle identifies Gillispie's book as an account of the impact of scientific discoveries upon religious beliefs in the decades before Darwin.

Probably the best brief review of the intellectual progress and development of mankind is J. Bronowski, 1973, *The Ascent of Man,* Little Brown and Co. This excellent book has been adapted for a 13-part television program that has been viewed by millions. A list of recommended readings may be obtained from stations showing the series.

2

𝕻𝖗𝖔𝖇𝖊 𝕬𝖑𝖑 𝕿𝖍𝖎𝖓𝖌𝖘...

The creation scriptures are undeniably controversial. Over the centuries they have generated belief, doubt, and differences of opinion. To some they have been faith-promoting, to others faith-destroying, always a challenge, ever an enigma. Could it be that these scriptures are intended to present another opportunity for the exercise of faith? Genesis by itself it not sufficient to win believers but neither is it sufficient to turn them away. Perhaps it is not far from the truth to say that in the present age of science most of those who believe in the Old Testament do so in spite of Genesis rather than because of it. The difficulties that face traditional literal interpretations have grown with time until they seem insurmountable. A list of the less trivial and more widely expressed arguments against the creation scriptures must include at least the following:

1. It is impossible for any human writer or writers to have knowledge of the prehistory of the earth or the development of the universe before these subjects had been investigated scientifically.

2. There are apparently two conflicting accounts of creation, one in the first chapter of Genesis, the other in the second chapter. These differ in emphasis and in the order of the creative events. Although there appears to be a transition between the two accounts in the first few verses of Genesis 2 these verses make little sense and could be nothing more than a clumsy attempt to fuse material from two different sources.

3. Certain elements of the Genesis account are found in creation-myths of non-Hebraic people. These stories involve episodes and personalities that are difficult to accept as anything but human inventions. Genesis might thus be only a more cleverly contrived but still human account of how things came to be.

4. If taken literally the story is that the totality of material things was brought into being in six 24-hour days about 6,000 years ago. Even though other scriptures are sometimes cited to possibly lengthen the creative days to 1,000 years each this is not convincing. How can this "quick creation" interpretation be reconciled with good evidence that the earth is billions of years old and the universe many times older?

5. Although the Genesis account is clearly sequential and tells of 6 creative periods these cannot be reconciled with the recognized epochs, periods, or eras of geologic history. Geologists have

given up trying to correlate the record of scripture with the record of the rocks. Since science appears to have overwhelming factual evidence to support a version of the history of the earth that is at variance with the Genesis story, it is the scriptures that must be in error.

6. The implication is that God created living things directly from non-living material most probably from the soil or ground. Since there were only six short creative days available there is no time for the evolutionary process which most students find reasonably in accord with the facts.

7. The fact that plant life is mentioned as having been created on the third day before the appearance of the sun on the fourth day. How can plants possibly exist without sunlight?

8. The statement that sun, moon and stars came into being after the earth, something entirely out of harmony with astronomical evidence that stars are of various ages—new ones are continually being created and some are many times older than the earth.

9. The implication is that each and every living thing was commanded to multiply "its own kind" endlessly with no possibility of one species giving rise to another. Again there is conflict with the doctrine of organic evolution. Incidentally, no provision or explanation is given for extermination or for fossils.

10. The assertion that the first woman, Eve, was made from a rib of the first man, Adam.

A paralleled list of reasons for believing in Genesis might include the following. This list can be no more fair, accurate or complete than the previous one. It is chiefly an index of what many believers consider important.

1. The entire scripture is the word of God, and Genesis, being an integral part of the Bible, cannot be excluded from a place of authority and respect.

2. Jesus Christ referred to the writings of Moses with favor, thus putting a stamp of divine approval on Genesis.

3. The fundamental message of Genesis—that God is the Creator—is compatible with the entirety of the Bible and with latter-day scripture as well.

4. The wording of Genesis is dignified, simple, confident, positive and straightforward with no extraneous or extravagant explanations, interpolations or apologies.

5. The Genesis account affirms one God (or one Godhead) and is free from the bizarre, multiple, contentious personalities of most creation myths.

6. The human beings depicted in Genesis are believable persons with the strengths and weaknesses of ordinary mortals. They have no semi-supernatural traits or aberrations of character such as mark most mythological beings.

7. The events of Genesis are sequential and cumulative and the sequence is what would be expected in any orderly progressive or evolving system. The creation is all-inclusive.

8. The creations mentioned in Genesis, both animate and inanimate, are derived from that which precedes them, they do not have existence in a vacuum.

9. No evidence has been found to certify a human origin for the creation scriptures—the alleged authorship of God has not been refuted.

10. The preservation of the wording and spirit of the creation story through centuries of translations and transcriptions bespeaks divine guidance as well as human integrity.

Comparison of these two lists emphasize a predictable fact: if a person believes in God, he is automatically predisposed to accept the scriptures or be willing to make excuses for their shortcomings. Conversely, if one does not believe in God, quite naturally he is less likely to accept supernatural elements in the scriptures. To be noted also among the objections is the predominance of items that are matters of factual nature while in the believers list matters of feeling or emotion are emphasized. This could be translated to mean that since most objections to the creation scriptures are of a factual nature they can be either proven or disproven by additional facts. This indeed seems to be born out historically, science which leans heavily on facts has yielded little that seems to support literal interpretations and much that disproves them. As told in the previous chapter, scientists of the 18th and 19th centuries tried valiantly but unsuccessfully to reconcile Genesis with natural history but have now largely abandoned the attempt.

At this point a third list is called for. It serves to introduce the remainder of this book and gives reasons why it has been written. My list is positive, it is a believer's list. The time seems right to reassess the evidences for the truth of the creation scriptures. And I must take the position that they are true. By this I mean they are the authentic and authoritative message of God and when understood properly, they do not contradict any fact or facts that have been or ever will be discovered by man. In making such an assertion I am guided chiefly by the thought that it is more important to try to discover the intent of the creation scriptures than it is to contend for a particular interpretation of their meaning. I am not ignoring the problem of the origin of these records. I accept them as the word of God. This removes the necessity of having to traverse a treacherous road that has been gone over many times in the past with no lasting benefits.

Certainly, the thing to do if one theory proves fruitless is to try another; this is the scientific method. The apostle Paul said it well: "Prove all things; hold fast that which is good." (1 Thes. 5:21). The postulate that the creation scriptures are a human invention has been accepted and built upon by many thinkers over the centuries— their contributions seem to have been negligible. The postulate that the creation scriptures were intended to instruct mankind in astronomy, geology, biology, and anthropology has likewise been accepted and argued by countless others, again without convincing results.

Fortunately, there are many who are unwilling to reject Genesis because it seems to fail in the face of the facts of science. They remain convinced that it has value as an assertion of the personality of God and his relation to man and the universe. Yet, in order to maintain their faith they must ignore much that is plainly stated or relegate these riddles to the realm of myth or allegory. But these believers are on the right road. Not the least important purpose of the creation scriptures is to prove that God is God and is the Creator of all that is. How better to demonstrate this than to make it unmistakably plain that he, God, indeed knows the end from the beginning? Significant also is the revelation that this foreknowledge need not be verified from hidden scrolls or secret caves. It has been there all along in the Bible for any man to read and ponder. As if for emphasis, Latter-day Saints have two additional accounts in the Pearl of Great Price which add unmistakable verifications.

Even more to be marveled at is the fact that the message, though cryptic and obscure, is neither a lie nor a deception. It is not complex allegory too deep to fathom and figurative phrases are rare. No one word or phrase describes the creation scriptures, they are a riddle, an enigma, a mystery, and a conundrum whose meaning is best arrived at by analyzing the internal construction and selecting which of a number of possible meanings of key words agrees best with the known facts. A scarcity of facts is the ever-present obstacle to understanding. At one time the scriptures were interpreted as supporting or even proving the concept of a flat earth. This erroneous belief, which held the status of an obvious fact, has been supplanted by the positive knowledge that the earth is round. The scriptures were not wrong, they were seriously misinterpreted. Those in authority who had insisted on their misinterpretations brought discredit to themselves and seriously weakened the influence of organized religion. Ever since Galileo religion has been on the defensive against science. The clear lessons of this episode are that it is unsafe to insist on one interpretation to the exclusion of all others and that the possibility of being wrong should always be taken into account.

What if the facts seem insufficient or circumstantial evidences is all there is to go by? This is the common everyday problem of science and one the scientific method is supposed to solve. The unbiased searcher picks his best inference or as the legal profession must frequently do, relies on the best evidence the case allows. This is what I have done—the results seem worth reporting.

I do not profess to know all the answers, there are riddles and subtleties that are beyond my understanding. There are layers of meaning yet to be rolled back when the facts are known. I cannot answer all the objections that have been brought forth by critics but I can answer enough of them to convince myself that there is nothing insuperable to belief and confidence in the creation scriptures. Likewise I cannot agree with all the reasons for belief that others profess but I can agree with enough of them to be comfortable in the presence of most believers. Here then are my reasons:

1. The original creation scriptures were allegedly dictated by God and allowing for certain subsequent human changes that have been corrected by latter-day revelation these scriptures have every indication of being exactly in the form God intended.

2. The creation scriptures are consistent with all other scriptures, both ancient and modern, in affirming the nature of God, his relation to man, and the purpose of earth life.

3. The recorded events are in a logical step-by-step sequence that is in full agreement with the findings of science regarding the cosmological history of the system from which the earth took form.

4. Emphasis throughout is on events that were necessary to bring the earth into existence and, contrary to traditional interpretations, much of that which is described belongs to pre-earth time rather than post-earth time.

5. Nothing is said which positively prohibits a belief in a great age of the earth, the spontaneous appearance of life, the production of species by evolution, or the derivation of man's physical body from lower forms.

6. The six days of creation are clearly stated to have been six periods of light and darkness having no specific time values. Such alternations are entirely permissable if not actually required by modern cosmological findings.

7. The two seemingly contradictory accounts of creation (i.e. as given in Genesis 1 and Genesis 2) are sequential and not parallel. Genesis 1 pertains to conditions before the earth was suitable for habitation while Genesis 2 comprises the entire subsequent history of the earth and its life. The transition from potential to actual life was the watering of the earth, an event of paramount importance in geologic history just as it is in scriptural history.

8. Properly interpreted the creation scriptures not only confirm the authentic findings of science but also affirm the creative role of God. This in effect removes all cause for conflict between those who are unable to find God at work in the ongoing material world and those who believe that he not only creates but also sustains the world in every detail.

9. Properly interpreted the creation scriptures leave no place for disbelief in God. The positive evidence that they reveal an accurate foreknowledge of truths that were incomprehensible to man until the attainment of specific and accurate information about heaven and earth leaves mankind with no alternative but to admit the authenticity of the scripture and the reality of God.

10. That there are two distinct levels of meaning, one suited for the earth-bound man of former ages and another suited just as well for the more fully informed space-oriented man of today, demonstrates the compassionate concern and superior intelligence of a benevolent God.

Like innumerable claims that have been made about Genesis in the past those of the foregoing list must be tested and tried. Hopefully, the evidence of succeeding pages will be given a fair trial.

Comments and References

Efforts to prove or disprove the creation scriptures have occupied innumerable minds over the centuries. Because these scriptures deal with very specific natural events most investigators have sought for proof or disproof in the natural sciences which deal with the past. The history of earlier searches is traced in such books as J. C. Greene, 1959, *The Death of Adam,* Mentor Books. Stephen Toulmin and Jane Goodfield, 1961, *The Fabric of the Heavens,* Harper; G. C. Gillispie, 1959, *Genesis and Geology,* Harper; and Arthur Koestler, 1959, *The Sleepwalkers,* Grosset and Dunlap.

In spite of the general failure of science to vindicate the creation scriptures the effort to do so goes on. Some believe that science needs to be reinterpreted within strict scriptural guidelines.

Books such as: *Up with Creation; Evolution: the Fossils Say No!, Science and Scripture vs Evolution; Bible Chronology and the Age of the World* have been recently published. Persons interested in these writings and this approach should contact the Institute for Creation Research, 2716 Madison Avenue, San Diego, California. By contrast, another class of writing reflects a desire on the part of scientists to reconcile their findings with Genesis by less strict and literal interpretations of its passages. In this category are: Enrico Cantore, 1977, *Scientific Man,* ISH Publications; and Wolfgang Yourgran, and A. D. Breck, eds. 1977, *Cosmology, History, and Theology,* a symposium published by Plenum Press.

Numerous theologians, including deep students of the Bible have come out in favor of reconciliation with science by moderating strict scriptural interpretations. Examples are: Langdon Gilkey, 1965, *Maker of Heaven and Earth,* Anchor Books; Ernst Benz, 1966, *Evolution and Christian Hope,* Doubleday; Alan Richardson, 1961, *The Bible in the Age of Science,* SMC Press Ltd. (London); and Raymond J. Nogar, 1961, *The Wisdom of Evolution,* SMC Press, Ltd. (London).

It is well to prove all things but it is obvious that lifetimes could be spent studying diverse and contradictory opinions. What is needed are unifying concepts; more synthesis, less analysis.

Only an Account of This Earth   3

Where in the stream of eternity does the Genesis story begin and how much of the totality of all possible things is it intended to survey? The meager record of the creation scriptures certainly seems to provide no satisfactory answers to the problems of ultimate origin that are raised by modern science and philosophy. A scoffer might say that the author of the creation scriptures gives no profound answers because he knows none. But there are other explanations. Consider carefully how Moses obtained his information. The record commencing with Moses 1:27 bears repeating:

"And it came to pass, as the voice was still speaking, Moses cast his eyes and beheld the earth, yea, even all of it; and there was not a particle of it which he did not behold, discerning it by the spirit of God.

And he beheld also the inhabitants thereof, and there was not a soul which he beheld not; and he discerned them by the Spirit of God; and their numbers were great, even numberless as the sand upon the sea shore.

And he beheld many lands; and each land was called earth, and there were inhabitants on the face thereof.

And it came to pass that Moses called upon God, saying: Tell me, I pray thee, why these things are so, and by what thou madest them?

And behold, the glory of the Lord was upon Moses, so that Moses stood in the presence of God, and talked with him face to face. And the Lord God said unto Moses: For mine own purpose have I made these things. Here is wisdom and it remaineth in me.

And by the word of my power, have I created them, which is mine Only Begotten Son, who is full of grace and truth.

And worlds without number have I created; and I also created them for mine own purpose; and by the Son I created them, which is mine Only Begotten.

And the first man of all men have I called Adam, which is many.

But only an account of this earth, and the inhabitants thereof, give I unto you. For behold, there are many worlds that have passed away by the word of my power. And there are many that now stand, and innumerable are they unto man; but all things are numbered unto me, for they are mine and I know them.

And it came to pass that Moses spake unto the Lord, saying: Be merciful unto thy servant, O God, and tell me concerning this earth, and the inhabitants thereof, and also the heavens, and then thy servant will be content.

And the Lord God spake unto Moses, saying: the heavens, they are many, and they cannot be numbered unto man; but they are numbered unto me, for they are mine.

And as one earth shall pass away, and the heavens thereof even so shall another come; and there is no end to my works, neither to my words.

For behold, this is my work and my glory to bring to pass the immortality and eternal life of man.

And now, Moses, my son, I will speak unto thee concerning this earth upon which thou standest; and thou shalt write the things which I shall speak.

The greatest and most basic questions of cosmology and philosophy are referred to here. The extent of space, the duration of time, the relation of space and matter, the multiplicity of worlds, the universality of human life, the fate of material entities both living and dead, and greatest of all, the purpose, design and meaning behind it. Moses saw the totality of it all but he did not understand it. And God in his wisdom kept the greater mysteries to himself and explained only a minor part to Moses. Furthermore, God gave strict instructions that only this minor part, pertaining to the earth and its heavens should be revealed. Why this restriction?

Somewhere the power of man's intellect seems to reach a limit. Anyone, from the unlearned savage to the erudite scholar, may contemplate infinity and eternity but as yet no one claims to understand them. If a human mind has ever existed which understood the full sweep of time and space, it has not succeeded in conveying its finding and conclusions to lesser minds. Full understanding might, in fact, be too much for the human brain to bear.

Although ultimate knowledge may be unattainable to earth-bound minds there has always been more than enough half-hidden mysteries beyond that which is known to intrigue the curious and invite the explorer. It is the challenge of the unknown that separates the venturesome from the timid. If the lessons of the past mean anything it is that knowledge advances by steps from the known to the unknown—this should give us confidence that we have not yet reached the limits of that which we may expect to learn and understand.

For the time being our task is made easier and our reward more certain if we take God at his word and interpret Genesis as an account of this earth-system only. By this we are assured of remaining within the bounds of human capability, we are spared of having to deal with the basic mysteries and we have some hope of understanding what was intended. Not everything about this earth is simple and clear—complex problems are likely to have complex solutions. Confronted with explaining the history of the earth (and its heavens) there is still a necessity of starting somewhere. Man's formalized departments of knowledge illustrate this. The astronomer begins his explanations with a universe of some sort in existence, the physicist starts with matter-energy already at his disposal. The usual geology text opens with the earth in its orbit. Biologists start with the simplest living things and anthropologists show little concern with anything antecedent to man. Even if the expert tries to get at the true origins of his subject matter, he is forced to disregard side issues and problems that lead elsewhere. The tree of knowledge has many branches, the shortest route from base of trunk to any particular leaf is along certain branches only. The others had best be ignored.

To describe the origin of the earth one cannot begin with an earth already formed. Questions about the previous history of the elements of which is it composed, about the dynamic systems to which it belongs and the forces and energy that keep it in operation beg to be answered.

Enough is revealed in the creation scriptures about these matters to encourage us to fill in the details, to caution us if we are on the wrong track and even to console us if there are mysteries we do not comprehend.

Comments and References

As a result of increasing understanding of matter and energy and the laws that govern them, science has now put together a reasonable picture of the origin of the universe. Although much of the detail remains to be worked out the broad outlines are not likely to be greatly altered by future discoveries. A reconstruction of the past is certainly one of the great triumps of the human mind. It has been achieved by reasoning from fact to fact, from cause to effect and without appeal to anything incomprehensible or miraculous.

Science does not profess to be able to determine goals or purposes in what it discovers. Scientists are dedicated to answering how but avoid telling why. It seems entirely possible that science will reach an end to what may be discovered by the scientific method and will still be silent on ultimate causes. To put God in the scene will remain, as always, the task of theologians.

This book makes no attempt to fathom the purposes of creation but does proceed on the assumption that there is a creator and he has a purpose as well as a plan. If there is any truth in the ideas that are expressed in following chapters, it has emerged only because the words given to Moses encourage the thought that the creation of this earth is comprehensible.

Write the Words Which I Speak 4

"And now, Moses, my son, I will speak unto thee concerning this earth upon which thou standest; and thou shalt write the things which I shall speak."

Moses 1:40

"And it came to pass that the Lord spake unto Moses, saying: Behold, I reveal unto you concerning this heaven, and this earth; write the words which I speak...."

Moses 2:1

Latter-day revelation certifies the origin of the Biblical Book of Genesis in an indirect but unmistakable way. Chapter 1 of the Book of Moses in the Pearl of Great Price is titled Visions of Moses and was revealed to the Prophet Joseph Smith in June, 1830. Chapters 2 to 8, completing the books, are titled Writings of Moses and were given to the Prophet in December of 1830. Chapter one contains the direct recorded words of God and is an explanation and introduction to what follows in the succeeding seven chapters.

The history of the Book of Moses seems to prove that it is to take precedence over any other equivalent scripture, including the King James Version. Joseph Smith received it as a direct revelation from God and evidently intended that it be incorporated in his translation of the Bible. Although the Prophet is not known to have left anything in writing that specifies the exact connection of the material of the Book of Moses and the Bible this material is included in all original Old Testament manuscripts of the Prophet's translations and stands at the beginning of all printed editions of the Inspired Version.[1]

Chapter one of the Book of Moses stands as an introduction or explanation of the remainder of the Moses record. It has no equivalent in any other translation of the Bible. Chapters 2 to 8 inclusive

---

1. It is under the name *Inspired Version* that Joseph Smith's translation has become generally known.

are in fact a re-revelation of the material of Genesis up to the time of the Flood. That there was need for such re-revelation is clearly explained in Moses 1:41:

> "And in a day when the children of men shall esteem my words as naught and take many of them from the book which thou shalt write, behold, I will raise up another like unto thee; and they shall be had again among the children of men—among as many as shall believe."
>
> Moses 1:41

We are informed in these scriptures that Moses saw God and talked to him face to face and that he also beheld visions of the creation of this and other worlds. Nevertheless, Moses was not allowed to describe his impressions and experiences in full. God's instructions are quite clear and explicit "...thou shalt write the things which I shall speak." (Moses 1:40), and also, "...write the *words* which I speak...." (Moses 2:1).

In view of these instructions we must conclude that the exact words given or spoken by God as recorded in the original Genesis and re-revealed in the Book of Moses are of paramount importance and are not to be altered or mistranslated to even the slightest degree. Those who believe in the sanctity of scriptures are quite right in insisting that they are intended to be translated and transcribed without alterations, deletions, or interpolations. Note that God in foretelling subsequent events declares that men will remove *words* from the writings of Moses. Again a reference to "words" that cannot be over emphasized. It will be observed when the King James and Joseph Smith translations are compared that the differences lie chiefly in what has been deleted or left out of the King James version. In most cases these omissions are single words or short phrases. These missing parts assume greatest importance as the remainder of this book should demonstrate. Can it be that more or less innocent meddling with words is what has happened in the past and is happening in the many new translations and versions that have appeared during the past century?

The Book of Moses leaves no doubt as to who wrote Genesis, why he wrote it and approximately when he wrote it. Moses is the author, he wrote it at the command of God ("the book that thou *shalt* write") and of course he wrote it during his mature lifetime about 1250 B.C. But more important than this is the fact that although Moses wrote the creation account he did so in the exact words of God ("write the *words* which I speak").

We may say the entire Bible is inspired and ponder the balance of human and divine influence that shows forth in its various books. But of this we can be certain, the creation scriptures as given in the Book of Moses are in the words of God and are not the fabrications of men.

The Book of Abraham which is bound with the Book of Moses in the Pearl of Great Price contains invaluable additions to the creation scriptures. As described in the introduction by Joseph Smith the Book of Abraham is "A translation of some ancient records that have fallen into our hands from the catacombs of Egypt.... The writings of Abraham while he was in Egypt, called the Book of Abraham, written by his own hand, upon papyrus." That the account of Abraham should convey the same facts as Genesis and Moses is expectable since all derive ultimately from the same source. The writing of Abraham must have preceded the writing of Moses but this does not make it necessarily more accurate or complete. Abraham learned with the aid of the Urim and Thummim. That he knew all the essential facts is obvious from his writings. Undoubtedly he knew much more but of the extent of this knowledge we can only speculate.

Of course Moses did not speak and write English and Joseph Smith did not repeat the message of Moses in the language of Moses or the message of Abraham in the language of Abraham. Nevertheless the exact meaning intended by God is there, otherwise God must be in danger of contradicting himself from age to age.

Statements of the Prophet Joseph Smith:

"From sundry revelations which had been received, it was apparent that many important points touching the salvation of men, had been taken from the Bible, or lost before it was compiled." *(Teachings of the Prophet Joseph Smith,* comp. Joseph Fielding Smith, Salt Lake City, Deseret Book Co., 1938, pp. 9-11.)

"I believe the Bible as it read when it came from the pen of the original writers. Ignorant translators, careless transcribers, or designing and corrupt priests have committed many errors." *(Ibid.,* pp. 290-91.)

Statements of President Brigham Young:

"The Bible is true. It may not all have been translated aright, and many precious things may have been rejected in the compilaton and translation of the Bible; but we understand, from the writings of one of the Apostles, that if all the sayings and doings of the Savior had been written, the world could not contain them. I will say that the world could not understand them. They do not understand what we have on record, nor the character of the Savior, as delineated in the Scriptures; and yet it is one of the simplest things in the world, and the Bible, when it is understood, is one of the simplest books in the world, for, as far as it is translated correctly, it is nothing but truth." (Journal of Discourses 14:135-136.)

"And I have heard ministers of the gospel declare that they believed every word in the Bible was the word of God. I have said to them "you believe more than I do." I believe the words of God are there; I believe the words of the devil are there; I believe that the words of men and the words of angels are there; and that is not all,— I believe that the words of a dumb brute are there. I recollect one of the prophets riding, and prophesying against Israel, and the animal he rode rebuked his madness.

Do you believe all this is the word of God? If you do, you certainly believe more than I do. The words of the Lord are the words of the Lord, and the revelations God has given concerning himself are true." (*Ibid.,* 14:280.)

Comments and References

Christ said that man should not live by bread alone but "by *every word* that proceedeth out of the mouth of God." Christ himself is referred to as the Word. The Bible is the very word of God. There are hundreds of verses in the Bible in which word is the subject. Through the ages men have insisted that every word of scripture be preserved intact in meaning and context. Scribes counted and recounted not only the words but the letters of their manuscripts to verify correct transcriptions. Small wonder that God when instructing Moses on the subject of Creation should insist that his exact words be set down. Now after centuries of time we see clearly why this was necessary.

That man, for the most part, has preserved the wording of Genesis intact is shown by the agreement of the various translations. Refer to Luther A. Weigle, 1952, *The Genesis Octapla,* Thomas Nelson and Sons. In this, eight English versions of Genesis are compared verse for verse and word for word. That there are scarcely any differences speaks highly for the integrity of the scriptures and the men who translated them.

Joseph Smith, modern prophet, was also impeccable in his translations. The excellent book, Robert J. Matthews, 1975, *Joseph Smith's Translation of the Bible,* Brigham Young University Press illustrates this. When the Bible account of creation is compared with the Book of Moses and Book of Abraham in the Pearl of Great Price, it is seen that here and there a word or a phrase has been omitted from Genesis. These omissions are critical. How and when they occurred is not clear but it is by the omission of mere words that Genesis became unclear and controversial. With these words restored in their modern scriptures Latter-day Saints should be at the forefront in understanding what God intended should be understood in the last days.

5

In The Beginning . . .

"In the beginning God created the heaven and the earth."

Genesis 1:1

"...I am the Beginning and the End, the Almighty God,... Yea, in the beginning I created the heavens and the earth upon which thou standest."

Moses 2:1

"And they went down at the beginning, and they, that is the Gods, organized and formed the heavens and the earth."

Abraham 4:1

Infinity and eternity are difficult if not impossible for the human mind to comprehend. It is much easier to deal with beginnings and endings because these are what we experience and observe every day. The world is one of finite things with edges, boundaries, dimensions, origins, endings, startings, stoppings, appearances and disappearances. Only when we gaze into the starry heavens do we begin to grasp, however dimly, the idea of infinity. But the same question that stirred the first inquiring minds thousands of years ago still plagues the sophisticated far-seeing scientist of today: what lies beyond? Always one can imagine a boundary but never a boundary with nothing behond.

The mind dwells more comfortably with the idea of a beginning than it does with no beginning. Two popular theories of the universe may illustrate this. The steady-state theory is that there was no beginning and will be no ending to the universe and the processes within it. What we observe today is a typical example of what could have been seen in the infinite past or might yet be seen at any stage in the infinite future. Stars are observed in process of birth and in every stage leading to their decay and death.

On the other hand is the big-bang theory—the very name is descriptive of an initiating event. At the time of the so-called big-bang, according to the theory, matter was concentrated in one region of space in the form of a compact mass or "super atom." So great is the compactability of matter that it is calculated that all the constituents of the known universe could be contained in a sphere no larger than that circumscribed by the solar system. At an instant of maximum compression this initial mass exploded with unimaginable violence sending matter and energy speeding outward in all directions to initiate a chain of events which is still in process.

The expansion of the universe is a matter of observation; in fact, it constitutes the strongest evidence for the big-bang theory. All other theories have had to adjust to it in one way or another. The steady-state theory admits that the galaxies are flying apart and concedes that if this has been going on indefinitely, they should be at infinite distances from each other. To overcome this difficulty it is proposed that matter from which new galaxies form appears in the spaces between the older ones. According to some, this new matter appears literally out of nothing. Perhaps this belief traces in part to the declaration in the Vulgate version of the Bible, so called from its common use in the Catholic Church, that God created the world out of nothing (2 Machabees 7:28). Many believe that new elements are reconstructed from the matter-energy poured into space by older suns and galaxies. Even within the framework of a no-beginning, no-ending universe there must be provisions for the undeniable beginnings and endings that are part of it.

A third concept that to some extent shields the mind from the awful concepts of sameness and endlessness is the oscillation theory. This admits all the facts of an expanding universe and the evidences for a big-bang beginning but envisions a time when expansion will be neutralized and the present universe will begin to contract. Ultimately another primeval atom will appear from which a new universe may emerge. This does not really settle the problems of eternity and infinity, it merely supplies punctuation marks, interruptions, or changes of scene that make eternity less monotonous.

The latest word from science (1978) is that the expansion of the universe as required by the big-bang theory is likely to continue indefinitely. Evidence from several sources is that the outward flight of matter cannot be reversed and the galaxies will continue to fly apart forever. Scientists who made this prediction realize that it could be revised by additional data at any time. The final word is really not in. At the present time the most distant galaxy known is 8 billion light years away; it must have formed at least 8 billion years ago.

In both ancient and modern scripture God is represented as endless and eternal, in fact it is in terms such as "without beginning of days or end of years" that he describes himself. The common Christian manner of addressing God is as the Eternal Father. Nothing in theology seems more firmly established than the eternal nature of God. Assuming this, what are we to understand about the "beginning" which the scriptures describe? Obviously this cannot be the beginning of God for he is endless, without beginning or end. Not the least of the mysteries about God is what he may have been doing before the creation. This is more of a problem if ours is the only creation with which God is concerned and from Genesis alone we might assume that this earth and its related heaven is the only one of its kind in existence. But modern scripture makes it plain that this is not so. As described in the Pearl of Great Price, Moses received a great vision of all the creations of God:

> "And it came to pass that Moses called upon God, saying: Tell me, I pray thee, why these things are so, and by what thou madest them?
>
> "And behold, the glory of the Lord was upon Moses, so that Moses stood in the presence of God, and talked with him face to face. And the Lord God said unto Moses: For mine own purpose have I made these things. Here is wisdom and it remaineth in me.
>
> "...And worlds without number have I created; and I also created them for mine own purpose;...
>
> "...But only an account of this earth, and the inhabitants thereof, give I unto you. For behold, there are many worlds that have passed away by the word of my power. And there are many that now stand, and innumerable are they unto man; but all things are numbered unto me, for they are mine and I know them.
>
> "And it came to pass that Moses spake unto the Lord, saying: Be merciful unto thy servant, O God, and tell me concerning this earth, and the inhabitants thereof, and also the heavens, and then thy servant will be content."
>
> Moses 1:30, 36.

The narrative continues with the description of the creation essentially as given in Genesis. Obviously God is concerned with endless creations of which ours is but one.

The great Mormon writer and scientist James E. Talmage has this to say regarding the beginning:

"...we are without information as to what stage of earth development is indicated by "in the beginning." And what is a beginning in nature? At best it is but a new start in advance of what has passed up to that point of time; and every beginning is an ending of what went immediately before, even as every consummation is a commencement of something, greater, higher, and therefore superior to the past."

We are spared the difficult if not impossible task of having to deal with incomprehensible infinity if we assume that the beginning mentioned in Genesis is a definite point in the stream of eternity when the Gods took action that ultimately resulted in the formation of this world. Scripture tells of a grand council in heaven "before the world was." Note that this was before the world was but not before man or God or presumably the elements were in existence.

Statement of Brigham Young:

"We understand, for it has been told us, that we had an existence before we came into the world.... We came here to live a few days, and then we are gone again. How long the starry heavens have been in existence we cannot say, how long they will continue to be we cannot say. How long endure, in their present combinations, it is not for us to say. Our religion teaches us that there never was a time when they were not, and there never will be a time when they will cease to be; they are here and will be here forever.

"I will give you a figure that Brother Hyde had in a dream. He had been thinking a great deal about time and eternity; he wished to know the difference, but how to understand it he did not know. He asked the Lord to show him, and after he had prayed about it, the Lord gave him a dream, at least I presume He did, or permitted it so to be, at any rate he had a dream; his mind was opened so that he could understand time and eternity. He said that he thought he saw a stream issuing forth from a misty cloud which spread upon his right and upon his left. He was told that the stream was time, that it had no place where it commenced to run, neither was there any end to its running; and that the time which he was thinking about and talking about, what he could see between the two clouds, was a portion of or one with that which he could not perceive. So it is with you and I; here is time, where is eternity. It is here, just as much as anywhere in all the expanse of space; a measured space of time is only a part of eternity."

Comments and References

Latter-day Saint students have a distinct advantage in knowing that what is revealed in the creation scriptures pertains only to this earth. It seems safe to assume that this means we have been given information going back to the beginning of the system from which the earth emerged. Even though this is a vast subject and covers an immense time span it does save us from fruitless searching into matters that do not concern this earth. Among such mysteries are the meaning of eternity and infinity, the possibility of other universes and other gods, the problem of creation from nothing, the state of things before the beginning of our universe and the cause of its beginning.

Heeding the caution about avoiding the ultimate mysteries it is assumed that the "beginning" referred to in the first verse of Genesis is the beginning of our universe, an event described in scientific terms as the big-bang theory. This theory is mentioned and discussed in many astronomy texts and popular science articles. An excellent book by the man who had much to do with formulating, refining, and defending the theory is George Gamow, 1956, *The Creation of the Universe,* Viking Press. An updated description of the same events is Steven Weinberg, 1977, *The First Three Minutes: A Modern View of the Origin of the Universe,* Basic Books.

God Created

"In the beginning God created the heaven and the earth."

Genesis 1:1

..."I am the Beginning and the End, the Almighty God; by mine Only Begotten I created these things; yea, in the beginning I created the heaven, and the earth upon which thou standest."

Moses 2:1

"And then the Lord said: Let us go down. And they went down at the beginning, and they, that is the Gods, organized and formed the heavens and the earth."

Abraham 4:1

It seems entirely appropriate to refer to God as the creator but such reference perpetuates a misunderstanding of the whole subject of the Godhead and of the Creation. The simple assertion of Genesis that God created the heaven and the earth seems to imply that one personage alone was responsible and that this person is God the Father. This must certainly be the understanding of those who accept the Old Testament but not the New Testament.

The opening verse of the Gospel according to St. John identifies Jesus Christ as the Word, verifies his status as God, asserts his co-existence with God (the Father) and makes clear that he (Jesus Christ) is the creator who made all things.

"In the beginning was the Word, and the Word was with God, and the Word was God.

"The same was in the beginning with God.

"All things were made by him; and without him was not any thing made that was made."

John 1:1-3

Other scriptures verify this important point.

"God, who at sundry times and in divers manners spake in time past unto the fathers by the prophets,
Hath in these last days spoken unto us by his Son, whom he hath appointed heir of all things, by whom also he made the worlds;"

Hebrews 1:1-2

"For by him were all things created, that are in heaven, and that are in earth, visible and invisible, whether they be thrones, or dominions, or principalities, or powers: all things were created by him, and for him:"

Colossians: 1:16

"For we saw him, even on the right hand of God, and we heard the voice bearing record that he is the Only Begotten of the Father—
That by him and through him, and of him the worlds are and were created, and the inhabitants thereof are begotten sons and daughters unto God."

D & C 76:23-24

"Behold, I am Jesus Christ the Son of the living God, who created the heavens and the earth; a light which cannot be hid in darkness;"

D & C 14:9

"Behold, I am Jesus Christ the Son of God. I created the heavens and the earth, and all things, that in them are. I was with the Father from the beginning. I am in the Father, and the Father in me; and in me hath the Father glorified his name."

3 Nephi 9:15

"Therefore in the beginning the Word was, for he was the Word, even the messenger of salvation,

The light and the Redeemer of the world; the spirit of truth, who came into the world, because the world was made by him, and in him was the life of men and the light of men.

The worlds were made by him; men were made by him; all things were made by him, through him, and of him."

D & C 93:8-10

These are difficult concepts to reconcile with the idea that the God of the Genesis account worked alone at the creation. Some Christian sects accept Christ as the creator, others do not. This would seem to prove that the Bible in itself has, for one reason or another, been an insufficient guide in bringing a unity of thought on the matter. This is not to be wondered at since the whole topic of the nature of God is one of endless controversy. Modern scripture is explicit and plain: Christ has identified himself as the Creator. His specific role in the making of worlds, of men and all things is beyond question. Nevertheless, ancient and modern scriptures also agree in the truth that God, the Father, delegated the power and the authority of creation to Christ who carried out the actual work; "by mine Only Begotten I created these things."

Note that the account of Moses is in the first person—God the Father is speaking. The accounts given in Genesis and Abraham is in the third person. In Genesis, God is not identified as being either the Father or the Son and if the Creator be one or many is a matter of interpretation. The Book of Abraham is explicit, here a plurality of Gods is plainly revealed: "And they went down at the beginning, and they, that is the Gods, organized and formed the heavens and the earth." (Abraham 4:1.)

Who were the personalities present at and participating in the Creation? God the Father was there for in the Book of Moses he says "...by mine Only Begotten I created these things; yea, in the beginning I created the heaven and the earth..." (Moses 2:1); Jesus Christ was there, for in the Doctrine and Covenants he says: "Behold, I am Jesus Christ...who created the heavens and the earth...." According to Brigham Young (Journal of Discourses 1:51) Adam or Michael was there: "It is true that the earth was organized by three distinct characters, namely, Elohim, Jehovah. and Michael. the three forming a quorum." No statements in the Standard Works gives any information as to Adam's role in the creation.

Joseph Smith had important things to say about the plurality of Gods and the creation. In a sermon given in Nauvoo, June 16, 1844, he stated:

> "I will preach on the plurality of Gods. I have selected this text for that express purpose. I wish to declare I have always and in all congregations when I have preached on the subject of Deity, it has been the plurality of Gods. It has been preached by the Elders for fifteen years.
>
> "I have always declared God to be a distinct personage, Jesus Christ a separate and distinct personage from God the Father, and that the Holy Ghost was a distinct personage and Spirit: and these three constitute three distinct personages and three Gods. If this is in accordance with the New Testament, lo and behold! we have three Gods anyhow, and they are plural; and who can contradict it?
>
> ...
>
> "In the very beginning the Bible shows there is a plurality of Gods beyond the power of refutation. It is a great subject I am dwelling on. The word *Eloheim* ought to be in the plural all the way through—Gods. The heads of the Gods appointed one God for us; and when you take (that) view of the subject, its sets one free to see all the beauty, holiness and perfection of the Gods. All I want is to get the simple, naked truth, and the whole truth.
>
> "Many men say there is one God; the Father, the Son and the holy Ghost are only one God I say that is a strange God anyhow—three in one, and one in three! It is a curious organization. 'Father, I pray not for the world, but I pray for them which thou has given me.' 'Holy Father, keep through Thine own name those whom thou has given me, that they may be one as we are.' All are to be crammed into one God, according to sectarianism. It would make the biggest God in all the world. He would be a wonderfully big God—he would be a giant or monster. I want to read the text to you myself—'I am agreed with the Father and the Father is agreed with me, and we are agreed as one.' The Greek shows that it should be agreed. 'Father, I pray for them which Thou has given me out of the world,

and not for those alone, but for them also which shall believe on me through their word, that they all may be agreed, as Thou, Father, are with me, and I with Thee, that they also may be agreed with us,' and all come to dwell in unity, and in all the glory and everlasting burnings of the Gods; and then we shall see as we are seen, and be as our God and He as His Father. I want to reason a little on this subject. I learned it by translating the papyrus which is now in my house." (Teachings of the Prophet Joseph Smith, pp. 370-373.)

...

Other enlightening statements on the subject of the creation were made by Joseph Smith in the King Follett Discourse, a funeral sermon first published in the *Times and Seasons,* August 15, 1844. Excerpts follow; the whole discourse is closely related to the topic under discussion:

"In the first place, I wish to go back to the beginning— to the morn of creation. There is the starting point for us to look to, in order to understand and be fully acquainted with the mind, purposes and decrees of the Great Elohim, who sits in yonder heavens as he did at the creation of this world. It is necessary for us to have an understanding of God himself in the beginning. If we start right, it is easy to go right all the time; but if we start wrong, we may go wrong, and it be a hard matter to get right."

...

"I want to ask this congregation, every man, woman and child, to answer the question in their own heart, what kind of a being God is? Ask yourselves; turn your thoughts into your hearts, and say if any of you have seen, heard, or communed with him. This is a question that may occupy your attention for a long time. I again repeat the question—What kind of a being is God? Does any man or woman know? Have any of you seen him, heard him, or communed with him? Here is the question that will, peradventure, from this time henceforth occupy your attention. The Scriptures inform us that "This is life eternal that they might know thee, the only true God, and Jesus Christ whom thou hast sent."

...

"I shall comment on the very first Hebrew word in the Bible; I will make a comment on the very first sentence of the history of creation in the Bible—*Berosheit*. I want to analyze the word. *Baith*—in, by, through, and everything else. *Rosh*—the head. *Sheit*—grammatical termination. When the inspired man wrote it, he did not put the *baith* there. An old Jew without any authority added the word: he thought it too bad to begin to talk about the head! It read first, "The head one of the Gods brought forth the Gods." That is the true meaning of the words, *Baurau* signifies to bring forth. If you do not believe it, you do not believe the learned man of God. Learned men can teach you no more than what I have told you. *Thus the head God brought forth the Gods in the grand council."*

...

"In the beginning, the head of the Gods called a council of the Gods; and they came together and concocted a plan to create the world and people it. When we begin to learn this way, we begin to learn the only true God, and what kind of a being we have got to worship. Having a knowledge of God, we begin to know how to approach him, and how to ask so as to receive an answer. When we understand the character of God, and know how to come to him, he begins to unfold the heavens to us, and to tell us all about it. When we are ready to come to him, he is ready to come to us.

"Now, I ask all who hear me, why the learned men who are preaching salvation, say that God created the heavens and the earth out of nothing? The reason is, that they are unlearned in the things of God, and have not the gift of the Holy Ghost; they account it blasphemy in any one to contradict their idea. If you tell them that God made the world out of something, they will call you a fool. But I am learned, and know more than all the world put together. The Holy Ghost does, anyhow, and He is within me, and comprehends more than all the world: and I will associate myself with Him.

"You ask the learned doctors why they say the world was made out of nothing; and they will answer, 'Doesn't the Bible say He *created* the world?' And they infer, from the word create that it must have been made out of nothing. Now, the word create came from the word *baurau* which does not mean to create out of nothing; it means to organize; the same as a man would organize materials and build a ship. Hence, we infer that God had materials to organize the world out of chaos—chaotic matter, which is element, and in which dwells all the glory. Element had an existence from the time he had. The pure principles of element are principles which can never be destroyed; they may be organized and re-organized, but not destroyed. They had no beginning, and can have no end." (*Teachings of the Prophet Joseph Smith,* pp. 343-352.)

There is yet another official clarification of the subject of God and the creation. In 1916 the presiding authorities of the Church issued a special publication: "The Father and the Son: A Doctrinal Exposition by the First Presidency and the Twelve." Parts of this somewhat lengthy statement are appropriate here: "The scriptures plainly and repeatedly affirm that God is the Creator of the earth and the heavens and all things that in them are. In the sense so expressed, the Creator is an Organizer. God created the earth as an organized sphere; but He certainly did not create, in the sense of bringing into primal existence, the ultimate elements of the materials of which the earth consists, for "the elements are eternal."

Under the subtitle of this exposition: *"Father" as Creator* we read: "A second scriptural meaning of "Father" is that of Creator, e.g. in passages referring to any one of the Godhead as "The Father of the heavens and of the earth and all things that in them are" (Ether 4:7; see also Alma 11:38, 39 and Mosiah 15:4). "God is not the Father of the earth as one of the worlds in space, nor of the heavenly bodies in whole or in part, nor of the inanimate objects and the plants and the animals upon the earth, in the literal sense in which he is the Father of mankind. Therefore, scriptures that refer to God in any way as the Father of the heavens and the earth are to be understood as signifying that God is the Maker, the Organizer, the Creator of the heavens and the earth."

"With this meaning, as the context shows in every case, Jehovah, who is Jesus Christ the Son of Elohim is called "the Father" and even "the very eternal Father of heaven and of earth."

"...Jesus Christ, whom we know as Jehovah, was the executive of the Father, Elohim, in the work of creation...."

These are strong doctrines and one gets a feeling that Joseph Smith knew more about these deep subjects than he actually made known. Certain it is that with the passage of time his insights and knowledge about the creation and the creators become more meaningful and profound. When the world has assimilated what has been revealed, perhaps more will follow.

Comments and References

All persons who take Christianity, Judaism, or Islam seriously agree that God created the world but their philosophers argue endlessly as to whether or not he created it from nothing. Viewpoints about the creative role of God in relation to the material world (with references) are found under suitable entries in *The Interpreters Bible,* vol. 1, 1952; *The New Catholic Encyclopedia,* 1967; the *Catholic Biblical Encyclopedia,* 1959; *The Universal Jewish Encyclopedia,* 1941; *The Encyclopedia of Biblical Interpretations* (Jewish), 1953 and *The Encyclopedia of the Lutheran Church,* 1965.

Scientists are just as concerned with the origin of the universe as are theologians but with few exceptions they regard matter-energy as eternal and express no need to call on divine interventions to organize it. Several good books on cosmology are: Theodore G. Mehlin, 1973, *Astronomy and the Origin of the Earth,* W. C. Brown Publishers; Fred Hoyle, 1975, *Astronomy and Cosmology,* Freeman and Co.; Lloyd Matz, 1976, *The Universe: Its Beginning and End,* Scribners; Jay M. Pasachoff, 1977, *Contemporary Astronomy,* Saunders; and Iran R. King, 1976, *The Universe Unfolding,* Freeman.

A rare meeting of minds among scientists and theologians took place at a symposium on the origin of the universe and other cosmological problems held in Denver, Colorado, November 1974. Twenty-three papers resulting from this gathering have been published in a book: *Cosmology, History, and Theology,* Plenum Press, 1977. Bibliographies give access to diverse opinions on a wide variety of topics.

Investigators should be aware that cosmology is a field where practically all references before 1970 are likely to be outdated or superseded insofar as astronomical findings are concerned.

The Heaven and the Earth

7

> "In the beginning God created the heaven and the earth."
>
> Genesis 1:1

> "I am the Beginning and the End, the Almighty God, by mine Only Begotten I created these things; yea, in the beginning I created the heaven, and the earth upon which thou standest."
>
> Moses 2:1

> "And then the Lord said: Let us go down. And they went down at the beginning, and they, that is the Gods, organized and formed the heavens and the earth."
>
> Abraham 4:1

The introductory statements to the three scriptural accounts of creation are all different and yet not contradictory. Basic in them all is the assurance that God is the Creator. Furthermore, they leave no doubt as to the comprehensive scope of creation—the heaven and the earth were brought into being. Variations are minor, the Abraham version reads heavens, not heaven, and the Moses account specifies the earth to be "that upon which thou (Moses) standeth."

Of the three accounts the Book of Moses should carry the most authority for it purports to be in God's direct words and has the least possibility of having been altered in translations. Certainly it is to be preferred to the shorter and more obscure 10-word statement of Genesis 1:1.

If no other scriptures are considered, the meaning of these opening verses would seem to be clear and simple—the first things to be produced were the planet and its surroundings without limit and without restriction. However, serious study of the next few passages of either Genesis, Moses, or Abraham reveals what appear to be problems of meaning. These center on what is to be understood by the words earth and heaven.

The word earth has two chief meanings of about equal status and importance in current and probably ancient usage. In the first place earth designates the fragmental material making up the surface of the globe or landscape. In this sense it is approximately the same as soil or ground. The second usage designates the specific planet on which we live. In this usage the word is frequently but not always capitalized.

The word earth is also used to distinguish areas of dry land from sea or air. In most instances it is of no great importance to make a distinction and if a distinction is intended, the context in which the word is used makes clear which of several meanings applies. The real test of whether or not one meaning is more important than another is what the user intends. Of course, communication has failed if a speaker intends one meaning and his hearers or readers receive another.

This brings us to the question of which meaning applies to the word earth as it appears in various creation scriptures. When Moses was told he would be informed about the earth upon which he stood, it would seemingly make no difference if he understood it to mean the planet Earth or the ground or soil in contact with his feet. But there are other places where the intended meaning is far more important. Consider the first verse of Genesis: "In the beginning God created the heaven and the earth." Does the earth referred to here mean the planet as such or does it designate soil or ground or even perhaps solid matter generally? The second verse of Genesis would seem to furnish a significant clue. Here we are told that the earth was originally formless and void. It is easier to conceive of elemental matter as existing in a formless condition than it is to think of the planet earth as being formless. It is a central fact of geography and astronomy that the Earth has a very definite nearly spherical shape, this is what makes it a globe and a planet. In a "formless" condition it would not be Earth. From this it seems permissible to assume that the earth of Genesis 1 is solid matter in unorganized condition.

Consider now the term *heaven* which is used in the same sentence as a companion term to *earth:* "In the beginning God created the *heaven and the earth."* Just as there are two common meanings for earth so are there two for heaven: first it is the space or expanse that extends indefinitely above the Earth; second, it is the dwelling place of God. The first meaning is not very precise or specific chiefly because there are usually no limits designated. In some usages heaven seems to pertain to all of space (the starry heavens) in other places the term seems to refer to the space around our particular Earth. In some usages each heavenly body seems to possess its own heaven. What is to be understood by references such as these "...the heavens, they are many, and they cannot be numbered unto man; but they are numbered unto me, for they are mine." (Moses 2:37.)

The second usage of the word heaven designates the place where God resides. "The heavens is a place where God dwells and all his holy angels." (Alma 18:30.) Rightly or wrongly this brings to mind a specific locality. In the thinking of the ancients the location of God's abode appears not to have been known except that it is above the earth. For a flat earth this is an understandable concept, it is not very satisfactory for a round one. Modern revelation is very helpful in this respect for it reveals that God resides near Kolob which is a great star set to "govern all those which belong to the same order as that upon which thou standest." (Abraham 3:3.) Since this governing body is clearly not the sun it must be a great star at or near the center of a much greater system, most probably the galaxy.

With the well-supported assumption that two meanings for the word heaven are admissible it is well to take another look at creation scriptures. In the first verse of Genesis "heaven and earth" are companion or parallel terms. What usage of the word heaven is intended? If we had no more than the first verse we might not be able to tell, but what follows in verses 6 to 8 would seem to leave no doubt: "Let there be a firmament in the midst of the waters, and let it divide the waters from the waters.... And God called the firmament Heaven...." (Note that here in verse 8 the word heaven is capitalized.) If the literal specific Heaven here described as a product of the second day is God's abode, then the heaven of the first day is merely open space awaiting further organization.

Comments and References

The central problem of this chapter is one of word meanings or semantics. The scriptural text presents us with two words—heaven and earth—both of which have numerous meanings. *The Shorter Oxford English Dictionary* which defines terms chiefly on historical principles gives 10 definitions of the word *heaven* and 17 of the word *earth*. Science cannot tell us which of these definitions is intended in the creation scripture. However, careful attention to the sequence of creative events strongly suggests that the heaven of Genesis 1 must be the entirety of space or at least that part of space associated with God's creative works; earth, in the same vein, must be the material of which things generally are composed. In other words both terms are to be understood in their most general senses and not in the limited specific senses that are implied in later verses of the same chapter. These general meanings do not conflict with precise grammatical usage or scientific concepts.

Apparently the choice of meanings is left to the judgment of the student. A good comprehensive dictionary and bible concordance are helpful. Since the interpretations suggested in this chapter are entirely consistent with modern scientific theories of creation they will be put to the test in what follows.

Earth...Without Form and Void 8

"And the earth was without form, and void; and I caused darkness to come up upon the face of the deep;..."

Moses 2:2

"And the earth, after it was formed, was empty and desolate, because they had not formed anything but the earth; and darkness reigned upon the face of the deep,..."

Abraham 4:2

The second verse of Genesis 1, the second verse of Moses 2, and the second verse of Abraham 4 all refer to the same stage of creation but each is significantly different. These verses portray conditions that prevailed early in the process of creation. A number of very dramatic words are employed to describe the state of things including void, empty, desolate, dark and without form. Those who would put the account in familiar modern language might say things were chaotic. The word Chaos is from a Greek word meaning empty space. But the idea that nothing existed at this time is contrary to actuality—earth was there. But chaos has also been defined as a mixed mass without form or order; in some usages there is a suggestion that the disorder of chaos has arisen from a previous state of order or that the disorder is temporary, pending attention and organization.

Void is a curious term with a number of meanings. It may designate that which is empty, vacant or not occupied; the emptiness it describes may be due to the lack of inhabitants or possessors. Void .nay signify the condition of being without something specific such as life or meaning. Also it may mean not productive of any effect or being in vain. These meanings are all in a different vein from the legal definition which means not binding, null or without effect.

65

Empty is a synonym of void with many of the same meanings such as containing nothing, being destitute, not supplied, unfruitful, vacated, meaningless, and unoccupied. The word desolate is used in the Abraham account. It carries slightly different meanings such as dreary, forsaken, deserted, uninhabited, or deprived of inhabitants.

The earth or earth material is also described as being formless. The improbability of a formless planet has already been discussed and the conclusion reached that the earth referred to in these introductory verses is unorganized matter in general and not the planet Earth. To refer to a planet as being without form is self-contradictory. It is the fact that Earth has a form which makes it a planet and not a shapeless mass. A planet might be void but not formless. However, an unorganized mass of matter can be both formless and void at the same time. Such distinctions are helpful in choosing between the two definitions of earth that are permissible at this point.

Comments and References

A basic belief of scientists who deal with matter is that it is composed basically of a relatively few fundamental or elemental units. Physicists are devising expensive and complex equipment and experiments to take matter apart and put it back together in order to learn more about the so-called subatomic particles. The electron and proton, formerly thought to be indivisible and irreducible, have been divided and reduced and the end may not yet be in sight.

No one doubts that the elemental units of matter-energy began to be assembled at the beginning of the universe. A very satisfying aspect of the big-bang theory is that it makes provision for the creation of the first atoms of hydrogen, simplest of the chemical elements, on a massive scale within the first few minutes of time. Following this for millions of years there was little more than hydrogen in the universe. The assembly of heavier, more complex elements had to await the appearance of the dense aggregations known as galaxies. The interval of quiescence, with hydrogen atoms dispersing outward in utter darkness is perfectly described by the phrase "without form and void."

Any good physics text has chapters on the structure of matter and its relation to energy but the subject is moving ahead so rapidly that text-book writers cannot keep up with the latest discoveries. The cosmic beginnings as visualized by astronomers are described in many books; two are Steven Weinberg, 1977, *The First Three Minutes: A Modern View of the Origin of the Universe,* Basic Books;

and George Gamow, 1956, *The Creation of the Universe,* Viking Press. Gamow is credited with developing the big-bang theory to its present level of high credibility.

9

Darkness...Upon the Face of the Deep

"And the earth was without form, and void; and darkness was upon the face of the deep. And the Spirit of God moved upon the face of the waters."

Genesis 1:2

"And the earth was without form, and void; and I caused darkness to come up upon the face of the deep; and my Spirit moved upon the face of the water; for I am God."

Moses 2:2

"And the earth, after it was formed, was empty and desolate, because they had not formed anything but the earth; and darkness reigned upon the face of the deep, and the Spirit of the Gods was brooding upon the face of the waters."

Abraham 4:2

The second verses of Genesis, Moses and Abraham are different from each other and yet not contradictory. Moses and Abraham add very significant details to the bare essentials of Genesis. Considered together they provide information fundamental to an understanding of the earlier phases of creation.

Always to be born in mind is that these scriptures pertain to the system of which the Earth is a member or from which it would ultimately emerge. This thought makes many things much more understandable than they would otherwise be. Consider the references to darkness. In human experience darkness is the opposite of light. Darkness is not usually thought of as being created—it is the inevitable state of things when and where there is no light. One does not usually think about darkness being created to overcome light but rather light being created to dispel darkness. It is only natural to conclude that darkness was the original primeval state of things and to believe that the entire universe was in a state of darkness before God commenced his work. And yet scriptures suggest that this is not necessarily so.

This possibility arises from the assertion in Moses 2:2 that God "caused darkness to come up upon the face of the deep." Darkness can replace only its opposite and that is light—the darkness referred to must have been preceded by light. Furthermore, the elimination of light was an essential part of creation and was brought about by the direct intervention of God. The command: let there be light was evidently preceded by one even more necessary and just as fundamental, let there be darkness!

The thought is not totally beyond experience. Every plant needs light to grow and develop and yet it cannot begin to grow in the presence of light. Only in the darkness of the soil will a plant germinate and only in the still darker interior of the seed will the embryo begin to swell. Every seed in effect must be taken out of light and placed in darkness before it can fill the really important part of its existence. The egg is a symbolic object to the mystical mind and an unsurpassed example of evolutionary adaptation to the scientist. Within its dark interior occurs one of Nature's most amazing transformations and nothing is more dramatic than the hatching process with a new being emerging into the light to begin a totally new phase of existence.

And so with ourselves. It is in the darkness of our mother's body that we begin life—in the darkness of the womb we grow until we are ready to come forth. The ancient phrase "seeing the light of day" is almost synonymous with being born.

That there must have been an interval of darkness in the creation of the universe is an essential requirement of the big-bang theory. This stage occurred between the production of the chemical elements in the big bang and their condensation into light-generating galaxies. Darkness took over when the powerful radiant energy of the initial explosion had faded and was no longer strong enough to prevent gravity from asserting its influence. Gravity is a weak force among smaller entities of matter but a strong and dominating one when the entirety of the universe is considered. Slowly and in total darkness the widely dispersed atoms of elemental hydrogen and helium were drawn into immense formless clouds. Centers of gravity with maximum density of matter were established in each such cloud and the stage was set for more spectacular developments.

Another thought emerges from the subject matter of the text. The term "face of the deep" is repeated in all three creative accounts. What is to be made of this? No matter how the term face is used it calls to mind something solid, or at least something with form behind the face. Thus we refer to the face of the land, or the face of the Sun or of the Moon; and, of course, a human face implies a head and body. Perhaps the reference, face of the deep, is to signify that there was a mass, at least a separate entity, with a surface or a discontinuity surrounding that which God intended to organize.

Scientists are fond of using the word interface and they know well enough that it is at the interface of things that physical and chemical actions take place. Erosion and weathering take place at the interface of land and atmosphere or between land and water; evaporation is a phenomenon of the interface of water and atmosphere. Exchange of heat and cold goes forward across interfaces, ice melts and water freezes at an interface. And chemical reactions even rapid explosions progress along a face or front. Life itself, most complex expression of natural processes, operates by reactions at interfaces provided by cell walls and interior membranes. An interface implies heterogeneity and heterogeneity is prerequisite to reaction. Not much, if anything can go on in a homogeneous state. The expression "face of the deep" implies the possibility of action and reaction yet to come.

Comments and References

According to the widely accepted big-bang theory of the origin of the universe the event that started it all was the explosion of a compact mass of elemental material that sent matter and radiant energy speeding headlong into space. So powerful was the energy released at this time that gravity could not assert itself and matter was dispersed and prevented from combining into solid entities of any kind. At length, however, as the initial energy was dissipated widely into space, its effects were weakened, light faded and darkness prevailed.

The ensuing period of universal darkness is a recognized phase of all versions of the big-bang theory. In the time span of creation it was relatively short—a matter of only about 100,000 years. Although this was a time of relative quiet what went on was essential to the on-going development of the universe. The most important effects came as gravity asserted itself and the widely dispersed hydrogen atoms began to draw together into clouds of ever-increasing density. These great aggregations, at first formless and void, were destined to become the galaxies within which light would once again be a dominant force.

Of all inclusive theories in science none can be said to have withstood the test of vigorous examination better than the big-bang theory. It is complex in detail but simple enough to be readily explainable and comprehensible on a popular level. Many good books and articles are available: George Gamow, 1956, *The Creation of the Universe,* Viking Press; Isaac Asimov, 1966, *The Universe,* Discus Books; James A. Coleman, 1963, *Modern Theories of the Universe,* The New American Library; Steven Weinberg, 1977, *The First Three Minutes: A Modern View of the Universe,* Basic Books. George Gamow is credited with establishing the big-bang theory on a firm theoretical footing; Isaac Asimov is a foremost popularizer of scientific subjects; James Coleman's book is notable for a simplified but comprehensive and unbiased presentation of competing theories; Steven Weinberg gives an updated account that integrates new findings and thinking about the first few minutes of creation.

10

The Spirit of God

"In the beginning God created the heaven and the earth.

And the earth was without form, and void; and darkness was upon the face of the deep. And the Spirit of God moved upon the face of the waters."

Genesis 1:1-2

"...I am the Beginning and the End, the Almighty God; by mine Only Begotten I created these things; yea, in the beginning I created the heaven, and the earth upon which thou standest."

And the earth was without form, and void; and I caused darkness to come up upon the face of the deep; and my Spirit moved upon the face of the water; for I am God."

Moses 2:1-2

"And then the Lord said: Let us go down. And they went down at the beginning, and they, that is the Gods, organized and formed the heavens and the earth.

And the earth, after it was formed, was empty and desolate, because they had not formed anything but the earth; and darkness reigned upon the face of the deep, and the Spirit of the Gods was brooding upon the face of the waters."

Abraham 4:1-2

In the first verse of Genesis we read of God and in the second we read of the Spirit of God. These two references raise important and interesting problems with regard to both the nature of God and the creative process. Is there a serious purpose in making a distinction between God and the Spirit of God or is this merely a literary embellishment or alliteration to add interest and variety?

What is to be understood by the Spirit of God as it is referred to in connection with the creation? In Latter-day Saint theology the Spirit of the Lord or Spirit of God has three different meanings:

72

(1) The spirit body of Christ, the body he possessed before he entered mortality; (2) the emanation of power and influence from God which fills space and by which he controls and governs all things; (3) the Holy Ghost, who is the spirit member of the Godhead. Such terms as Spirit, Holy Spirit, Spirit of the Lord, Spirit of God and Spirit of Truth are not always interchangeable or equivalent but the intended meaning is usually made clear by the context.

Of the three meanings cited above only the second can possibly apply to the creation accounts of Genesis, Moses and Abraham. The usage leaves no doubt as to whose spirit is referred to, "...*I* caused darkness to come up upon the face of the deep; and *my* spirit moved...." God the Father is speaking.

Writing on this subject Joseph F. Smith makes this helpful comment:

> "The Spirit of God which emanates from Diety may be likened to electricity or the universal ether which fills the earth and the air and is everywhere present. It is the power of God, the influence that he exerts through all his works, by which he can effect his purposes and execute his will, in consonance with the laws of free agency which he has confirmed upon man."

This seems to be a perfect description of the power which was operating at the creation. If it says anything, it is that there is a controlling influence which God exerts anywhere and upon anything to carry out his will. It is not necessary that he be personally present at any given time and place to accomplish his purpose.

The idea that there is a Spirit of God will be especially troublesome to those who believe that God is simply and exclusively spirit. They refer to the scripture which says: "God is a spirit; and they that worship him must worship him in spirit and in truth." (John 4:24.) But how can a spirit have a spirit? The Catholic belief as expressed in the information booklet, *"The Lessons of Genesis,"* is that "God is pure spirit; in Him there is nothing material" (Page 6). In the context of the present discussion the following quotation from the same source is significant: "Throughout the Old Testament period spirit of God simply means God Himself especially as He is life-giving" (Page 6). Incidentally the Vulgate translation of the Bible widely used by Roman Catholics reads, "the spirit of God was stirring above the waters." The explanation of this passage in the *Lessons of Genesis* is that "...we have here a picture of the creative power of God blowing over the unorganized elements of Creation like a mighty wind" (Page 5).

The Jerusalem Bible reads: "...And God's spirit hovered over the water." Billy Graham's version is: "...the earth was at first a shapeless, chaotic mass, with the Spirit of God brooding over the dark vapors." Some of these renditions may depart from the intended meaning so far as to be mistranslations. Incidentally, one wonders why the Billy Graham Bible uses the word brooding—it is the word translated by Joseph Smith from the scrolls of Abraham.

It can be only another manifestation of the wisdom of God that he revealed this important fact about himself very early in scripture, namely, that he is not a spirit. If men had understood this, or rather, if they had not rejected or forgotten it at an early date, much of the erroneous thinking, hurtful arguments and continual fragmentation of Christianity would have been avoided.

Historically, when early Christianity came into contact with the learned world the great philosophers had already concluded that matter being the basis of all visible things must also be the seat of evil; matter is basically evil. Consequently, the Supreme Being in order to be perfect must be immaterial, hence a spirit. And a spirit if it is immaterial, defies definition or understanding. It was also a foregone conclusion of the philosophers that God is surely not a man and not in the form of a man. Also, if there must be a great first and final cause, there can be only one such Being. This last teaching made the acceptance of Jesus as God almost impossible on a rational basis.

Over the centuries traditional Christian theology became so entangled in the coils of erroneous thinking that simple truths could no longer be accepted. Joseph Smith discovered that God is an exalted man, that all is material, even so-called spirit, and that there are many Gods. These truths were not new; the seeds of proper understanding had long been available in the first few verses of Genesis.

Comments and References

The subject matter of this chapter touches on the very nature of God and the Trinity because the allusion to both God and the Spirit of God may be interpreted in several ways. The belief that more than one personality participated in the creation is unquestioned by Latter-day Saints. Other bible-based churches who do not share the concept of a plurality of gods must interpret the Spirit mentioned in Genesis 1:2 in an entirely different way.

This is a vast and complex subject. An interested person should read about comparative beliefs regarding God. Good summaries are available under headings such as God, Holy Spirit, Holy Ghost, Creation, etc. in *The Interpreters Bible,* vol. 1, 1952; *The New Catholic Encyclopedia,* 1967; the *Catholic Bible Encyclopedia,* 1959; *The Universal Jewish Encyclopedia,* 1941; *The Encyclopedia of Biblical Interpretations* (Jewish), 1953; and *The Encyclopedia of the Lutheran Church,* 1965.

The Latter-day Saint understanding of the nature of creation and the personalities taking part in it are briefly discussed in the semi-official compilation, *Mormon Doctrine,* Bruce R. McConkie, Bookcraft, 1958. Entries that bear on the subject are Spirit of the Lord, Holy Ghost, Godhead, Trinity, Creation, and Word of God.

11

Upon the Face of the Waters

"...And the Spirit of God moved upon the face of the waters."

Genesis 1:2

_____

"...and my Spirit moved upon the face of the water; for I am God."

Moses 2:2

_____

"...and the Spirit of the Gods was brooding upon the face of the waters."

Abraham 4:2

_____

The first sentence of the creation scriptures names two created things, namely, heaven and earth. For each of these more than one definition is possible. Earth may be the planet of man's habitation or it may be solid matter generally; heaven may be the specific place where God resides or it may be space generally. What follows after the first verses strongly suggests that the broader more general meanings of both terms are intended. The first act of creation was to produce space and visible matter and not the planet earth and nearby space.

The second sentence of the creation scripture introduces another term for which there is only one definition and this presents difficulties. The term is water. What is to be understood by the term "face of the water," or "face of the waters," that occurs in the accounts? There is ample reason or excuse for the traditional view that the water or waters referred to must be the only deep water we know much about, namely, that contained in the oceans of the earth. But this cannot be if the earth of the preceding verse (Genesis 1:1), is not the planet Earth. It is as simple as this: no planet, no oceans. And while we are thinking about possible meanings, why is the term "face of the deep" used in the preceding sentence as if there were two faces or materials or conditions to be seriously considered?

Significant answers emerge when earth-centered interpretations of things are replaced with space-oriented ones. Brief mention must be made of what has been discovered in extra-terrestrial environments. In addition to solid bodies of various kinds the galaxy contains much gas and dust referred to as interstellar matter or the interstellar medium. This consists of matter left over from star formation and also of matter expelled from former stars as they exploded or disintegrated. Generally interstellar matter is so thinly dispersed that there is only one atom or molecule per cubic centimeter or so but there are other aggregations which may be spoken of literally as dense clouds. Interstellar clouds are transparent to varying degrees, some are so dense that they appear as vast, utterly dark patches; others are self-luminous, while still others appear to shine because there are suns burning deep within them.

Study of interstellar material is advancing rapidly chiefly because of recent developments in radio astronomy. By study of microwave measurement the elements and molecules present in space can be identified even though they give off no visible radiation. Results have been surprising, the number of interstellar molecules is 40 at the time of this writing and the list will certainly grow with time.

Among the molecules so far identified are the cyanogen radical, CN; hydroxyl radical, OH; ammonia, NH_3; water H_2O; formaldehyde, $H_2C{=}O$; carbon monoxide, CO; hydrogen, H_2; hydrogen cyanide, HCN; cyanoacetylene, $HC{=}C{-}CN$; methyl alcohol, CH_3OH; formic acid, $HCOOH$; carbon monosulfide, CS; formamide, $HC(NH_2)O$; silicon monoxide, SiO; carbonyl sulfide, OCS; acetonitrile, $CH_3C{=}N$; isocyanic acid, $HN{=}C{-}O$; methylacetylene, $CH_3C{=}CH$; acetaldehyde, CH_3CHO; thioformaldehyde, $H_2D{=}S$; hydrogen sulfide, H_2S; and methyleneimine, $H_2C{=}NH$. In late 1976 acetylene, C_2H_2 was discovered by infrared radiation. Infrared emissions can be detected in broad daylight and probably many new molecules will be found by this means. Some astronomers are convinced that almost any complex molecule can exist in space. We are finding only those which make their presence known by one means or another.

The study of the chemistry of interstellar material is clearly just beginning but what has already been discovered is very significant in any thinking about the origin of the earth. Even before the identification of specific elements and compounds in the clouds of space it was fairly well established that these clouds are the raw material out of which stars are formed. Now that some of the constituents of these clouds have been identified we know at least some of the potential building blocks of the earth and its neighbors. We say *some* of the blocks because there are many elements and even more compounds that cannot make their presence known to earth-bound observers. This is especially true of dust as compared to gas. Dust particles may have almost any composition and may be crystalline or non-crystalline, magnetic or non-magnetic, and of course have a wide range of possible reactions to radiation.

The present discussion may be restricted to water (H_2O) and to the hydroxyl component (OH) with which it is commonly associated. The hydroxyl radical was discovered in space in 1963, and water in 1969. Ammonia (NH_2) was identified in 1968. The presence of water and ammonia is not surprising since hydrogen is the most common element in the universe and the reactive elements oxygen and nitrogen are also abundant. Both water and ammonia solidify at relatively high temperatures, astronomically speaking, and it is supposed on indirect evidence that much of the dust in certain clouds is in the form of ice. In other areas water must occur as droplets in liquid form; under higher temperatures the gaseous state must prevail.

When I commenced to write this book, the amount of information on water in space was so limited my discussion was almost without foundation. Water was discovered in space in 1969, advances since then have been almost unbelievable. It is gratifying that discoveries are favorable to my interpretations.

Water makes itself known to astronomers chiefly because it can be stimulated under certain conditions to radiate detectable energy in wave-lengths beyond or longer than those visible to the eye as light. It is not a simple matter—the water molecule H_2O radiates only because it can operate as a maser (microwave amplification by stimulated emission of radiation). A maser operates when molecules, such as water, absorb energy from infrared (heat) sources and re-radiate the extra energy thus acquired in radio waves. It is a process of amplification or as it is commonly called, a pumping action. The maser reaction operates only when special conditions prevail. Temperature limits which favor the process are in the range 20 to 1000 K and the concentration of molecules is relatively low.

As it turns out the conditions under which water vapor can act as a maser are those associated with early (cooler) stages of star formation. The entire subject is relatively new. The association of

H2O masers and OH (hydroxyl) masers with early stages of star formation was not appreciated until the mid 70's. It is most exciting to know that elements and even compounds such as water can now be positively identified in space. Great new instruments such as radio telescopes and interferometers are being constructed with the potential of gathering as much information in the future as that gained in the past by the optical telescope. What can be said at this time merely introduces a subject destined to grow rapidly in importance in the years ahead.

The connection with creation scriptures is this: water exists in the clouds of space and is known to be abundant in areas where new stars are forming. Reasoning and speculating from these facts it may be assumed for the sake of continuing the story that water is essential to the formation of solar systems like the one to which the Earth belongs. In any event the earth is well supplied with water and must have emerged from a water-rich environment. Of course, it is realized that the original cloud contained many other substances besides water, some perhaps in amounts greater than water. But the original mix, no matter what the composition, could well be called water or at least water-like in physical and chemical properties. As described in the previous chapter the waters had a "face" implying their existence in a body separated from space or from material of another sort. This description agrees with what astronomers regard as a protocloud from which a sun-planet system might emerge.

Comments and References

Water (liquid, gas, or solid H_2O) has recently been discovered in space and may, in fact, be a major component of many great cloud-like aggregations.

Several books that treat the subject of water and other substances in interstellar space are: Neale Watson, 1973, *The Dusty Universe,* Academic Publications; Beverly L. Lynds, 1976, *Dark Nebulae, Globules, and Protostars,* University of Arizona Press; T. De Jong and A. Maeder (eds.), 1977, *Star Formation,* International Astronomical Union Symposium No. 75, D. Reidel Publishing Company; Cyril Ponnamperuma (ed.), 1976, *Chemical Evolution of the Giant Planets,* Academic Press.

Representative papers ranging from popular to technical include: Dale F. Dickinson, 1978, Cosmic Masers, *Scientific American,* vol. 238; George H. Herbig, 1974, Interstellar Smog, *American Scientist,* vol. 62, No. 2; H. C. van de Hulst, 1953, "Empty" Space, *Scientific American,* vol. 188, No. 6; K. J. Johnson, S. K. Knowles, and P. R. Schwartz, 1972, Microwave Celestial Water-Vapor Sources, *Sky and Telescope,* vol. 44, No. 2. A recent statement on the subject is R. Genzel and D. Downes, 1977, H_2O in the galaxy; sites of newly formed stars: *Astronomy and Astrophysics* Supplemental Series, A European Journal, vol. 30, pp. 145-168. This last named article describes 82 water vapor sources of which 32 are new discoveries. This research should eliminate any doubt as to the close relationship of water vapor and star formation.

12

Let There Be Light

"And God said, Let there be light: and there was light."

Genesis 1:3

_____

"And I, God, said: Let there be light; and there was light."

Moses 2:3

_____

"And they (the Gods) said: Let there be light; and there was light."

Abraham 4:3

_____

The glory of God is light and truth. God is a personage of light and it is in terms of light that he is described by those who have seen him. At his transfiguration it is declared that the face of Christ "did shine as the sun, and his raiment was white as the light." Moses encountered God in the bush that "burned with fire, and the bush was not consumed." Joseph Smith described the appearance of God the Father and Jesus Christ as being in "a pillar of light...above the brightness of the sun." He also declares that their "brightness and glory defy all description." The Prophet and Oliver Cowdery portray the Lord as he appeared to them in the Kirtland Temple:

> "The veil was taken from our minds, and the eyes of our understanding were opened.
> "We saw the Lord standing upon the breastwork of the pulpit, before us; and under his feet was a paved work of pure gold, in color like amber.
> "His eyes were as a flame of fire; the hair of his head was white like the pure snow; his countenance shone above the brightness of the sun...."

D & C 110:1-3

God is a personage of light and it is inconceivable that he could ever exist in darkness. As the Creator he must have brought forth light in many occasions before the event recorded in the third verse of the first chapter of Genesis. What then is to be understood by that profound utterance: Let there be light?

It cannot be without significance that darkness is mentioned before light in the creation scriptures. It is stated in Moses 2:2 that God "...caused darkness to come up upon the face of the deep." Light and darkness are opposites and antagonists as it were; when one prevails the other is absent. The coming of the darkness mentioned in scripture must have been marked by a corresponding withdrawal of light. Is the creation of darkness perhaps more important here than the creation of light? Strangely, scriptures tell nothing about the previous period of light, its radiance was fading when the first creative day began.

There are about 250 references to light in the Bible and 100 in the Book of Mormon. As might be expected these references relate to much more than manifestations of light in the physical sense. Light is often mentioned in connection with that which is spiritual or intellectual. Christ said: "I am the *light* of the world: he that followeth me shall not walk in darkness, but shall have the *light* of life." (John 8:12.) Light at least in scripture obviously has several basic meanings and the relation of physical light to spiritual things is beyond the scope of this discussion. Here we will concentrate on light as science describes it.

What is light? The author of the latest Encyclopedia Britannica article on the topic observes that light cannot be defined in terms of anything simpler or more directly appreciated by the senses than itself. Light has also been defined as a form of energy conveyed through empty space at high velocities. For practical purposes light is that manifestation of energy visible to the eye. According to another definition light is a form of electromagnetic radiation with wave lengths between about 310 and 1.050 millimicrons (from 16 to 30 millionths of an inch). Another definition is that it is energy contained in small packets called photons, a photon being regarded as a special type of fundamental particle.

These definitions introduce one of the great puzzles of science. Should light be considered as a wave or as a particle? In the early 19th century when many experiments were being performed with light, the wave theory held sway. Properties such as reflection, refraction and interference that are demonstrated routinely to all physics students are best explained as wave phenomena and can be duplicated by ordinary ripples in standing water. That light travels at the high velocity of 186,000 miles per second was demonstrated in 1927 but this did not settle the matter of whether it is a wave or a particle.

With the advent of atomic physics attention shifted to the problem of how light is created and destroyed or absorbed. Here the evidence favors the particle theory. The fact that there is a lower limit to the energy carried by light (3.5×10^{-12} erg or 3.5×10^{-19} joule) and that it is in this or multiples of it that all light can be described, gave rise to the necessity of dealing with it in terms of what are called photons. The concept that light must be regarded as an assemblage of entities was established by Albert Einstein in 1905. Later in the period of 1925-1930 the field of quantum mechanics appeared and has yielded a more unified view of what light is. In quantum mechanics light is not regarded strictly either as a particle or as a wave, the two are treated as compatible. The problem is when to regard light as a wave and when to regard it as a particle.

Unsolved as yet is whether the photon has weight or mass. It is the nature of light that it must be always in motion. Whatever it is that emerges as light is not light before it emerges; likewise, after it is absorbed, it is no longer light. This is a most critical point. Light can transmit information and energy across vast distances but can it transmit matter as well? It has not been proven that the mass of photon is absolutely zero; if it does have mass it must be exceedingly small. But if even the most minute quantity of matter is transmitted by light the over-all long-term effects are of great importance in the evolution of the universe.

Light is generated by atoms and molecules of many kinds when they are subject to outside influences such as application of heat, mutual crowding and the impact of radiation or other atoms and molecules. Light comes in different colors (wave lengths) and at different intensities. Variations in light are determined by the structure of the matter which generates it. Since the most abundant element is hydrogen this is the source of most of the light of the universe. Even though it is the simplest of the elements hydrogen can still give rise to light at a number of energy levels.

Matter not only generates light it also absorbs light. The existence of specific elements and compounds that occur in distant stars and galaxies is made know by characteristic ways in which these elements emit or absorb radiation. The study of this phenomenon is spectroscopy, the chief instrument of which is the spectroscope.

What light is and how it is created is a vast and complex subject to which only the barest introduction has been made in these paragraphs. To return to the topic under discussion we should inquire about conditions that prevailed on the first day of creation when under certain circumstances God said: Let there be light.

The appearance of light at a specific stage in the evolution of a typical galaxy such as ours is recognized as a critical event in all modern theories of the universe. This event holds a prominent place in the theory of the expanding universe which is the dominant or ruling theory at the present time. Light appears in a galaxy when an originally diffuse and lightless cloud of gas destined to become a galaxy reaches a sufficiently high state of compaction. As matter is forced into smaller and smaller space the electrons, atoms and molecules at the center of a protogalaxy collide with increasing frequency to generate radiant energy. At first only heat is produced, this is followed by a dull red glow which appears when the temperature reaches about 800 degrees Kelvin. Eventually, when the temperature reaches about 10,000,000 degrees Kelvin, thermonuclear reactions begin and a star is born.

It should not be inferred that the center of the galaxy is a great superstar in which the process just described takes place as a one-time, one-place event. The center of the galaxy as we perceive it at present is an area of many large, closely spaced stars together with clouds of dust and gas, the whole aggregation being the site of energetic reactions of many kinds. It should also be pointed out that the center of the galaxy is not observable by ordinary light because of the intervening dust. What we know and infer about it comes from infrared and radio waves which can penetrate the obstructing material.

The process of star formation began in the central core or hub of the galaxy where condensations first reached an effective stage of energy production. The process then spread outward and is still going on at a reduced rate where conditions are favorable. Obviously it had to begin at some time in the Milky Way Galaxy.

According to late versions of the big bang theory the formations of galaxies began about 100,000 years after the explosion of matter from the center of the universe. This period is not a long one in the astronomical sense but as described in chapter 13 many important and essential transformations took place during it.

It was after the lengthy period of universal darkness when the galaxies were in an early stage of condensation that God seems to have entered the scene. His agency in bringing forth light is not described in detail but what is revealed in scripture is thought-provoking. God's words were: Let there be light. The word, "let," is a significant clue. Aside from its usual meaning of giving permission let also means to allow or to remove restraints. Moses said to Pharaoh, Let my people go. In other words, remove their restraints or give your permission. God's agency in the production of light was to remove existing restrictions or to bring about conditions such that light might spontaneously appear. Darkness prevailed before God spoke or his spirit moved upon the face of the deep, then light appeared. With the appearance of light a new phase of creation began. Just how the words or actions of God might be explained scientifically is not clear but it would not seem to be an eternally impenetrable mystery, something that intelligent and righteous minds cannot comprehend. Perhaps no great reorganizations of latent matter and space were required to generate light at this critical stage. If the proper materials are already available, only a spark is needed to start a mighty furnace or ignite an everlasting flame. It was the intelligent application of power and authority at the right place and time that initiated the process of the generation of light as the most important event of the first creative period. The light was kindled at the center of the galaxy has continued to shine ever since like a great central fire. But other important appearances of light were to follow. Although it is not stated specifically light appeared and alternated with darkness on each of the six creative periods. This alternation is God's way of subdividing creation—he called the light Day and the darkness Night. The significance of this subdivision is a major theme of what follows.

Comments and References

Light is a universal phenomenon and the subject of much scientific research. Brief discussions that cover essential aspects of the subject as it is understood today are found in the latest editions of the Encyclopedia Britannica (1977) and Encyclopedia Americana (1977). All college and high school texts have chapters on light; current approaches are found in Virgilia Acosta, Clyde Harper and B. J. Graham, 1973, *Essentials of Modern Physics,* Harper and Row; Peter J. Brancazio, 1975, *The Nature of Physics,* Macmillan; George A. Williams, 1969, *Elementary Physics,* McGraw-Hill.

Books dealing specifically with light are: Vasco R. Ranchi, *The Nature of Light,* Harvard University Press; A. A. Sabra, 1967, *Theories of Light,* Oldbourne; and A. C. S. Van Heel and C. H. F. Velzel, 1968, *What Is Licht?* (English translation, *What Is Light?,* 1968).

The production of light is an innate capability of matter. The topic of the emission and adsorption of light is treated in general physics texts but no comprehensive non-technical discussion appears to have been written. The best discussion I have found is Trevor Weekes, Gamma Rays and the Origin of Cosmic Radiation: *Astronomy,* June, 1927; the illustration on page 8 is excellent.

A readable, well-illustrated book is *Light and Vision,* 1969, Life Science Library, Time, Inc. Other biological aspects of the subject are discussed in Life and Light, by George Wald, *Scientific American,* October, 1959.

13

God Divided the Light From the Darkness

"And God saw the light, that it was good and God divided the light from the darkness."

Genesis 1:4

"And I, God, saw the light; and that light was good. And I, God, divided the light from the darkness."

Moses 2:4

"And they (the Gods) comprehended the light, for it was bright; and they divided the light, or caused it to be divided, from the darkness."

Abraham 4:4

Light is the universal messenger not only from distant places but also from the distant past. The basic yardstick of astronomy, the light-year, is a measure of both time and distance. As telescopes gather light from the far off reaches of space they are also probing far into the past. With improvements in instruments and techniques astronomers are hoping to reach the edge of the universe. According to their best theories, if they can find this distant boundary, they will also be observing the beginning of the universe. The most distant object so far observed (1976) is said to be about 8 billion light years away. The universe is thought to be at least 20 billion years old.

But paradoxically the messages of light cannot be perceived without darkness. It is the interplay of the two which makes meaningful observation possible. The mind can imagine both a universe of light and a universe of darkness. Physicists can describe either of these as verifiable possibilities and can speculate why we live in a universe where both exist in so many interesting and contrasting ways.

It is not surprising that the whole story of creation is represented in terms of alternations of light and darkness. In the first stages of creation the contrasts are strongly emphasized in ways that challenge understanding and explanation.

We are informed that when Gods saw or comprehended the light, they preceded to divide or cause it to be divided from the darkness. But we are not told how this was done. To the earth-bound observer light is divided from darkness simply by the rising and setting of the sun. In ancient times it was the sun that did the moving, the earth stood still in the center of things. Later when the true nature of the solar system became evident, it was the rotation of the earth that was seen to divide the light from the darkness. In other words a purely mechanical process did the dividing. And it is this commonplace everyday earth-sun mechanism that probably comes to the mind of most readers when they try to visualize the original division of light from darkness. But that this cannot be the method of the first few divisions of the creative periods is apparent from the scriptures themselves—the sun did not appear until the fourth day.

There are many ways besides the revolution of the earth that light may be divided from darkness and even though the methods may not be correctly identified for each of the six successive creative periods there is no lack of interesting and varied possibilities. In the first place light may be divided from darkness strictly on the basis of time—one period may be entirely dark and another entirely light: that is, there might be universal darkness followed by universal light. Thus, light may have existed everywhere at the time of the birth of the universe to be succeeded by an all-pervasive darkness later on. Believers in the Big Bang theory think it is possible that after matter and radiation had become widely dispersed a condition of darkness prevailed generally for perhaps 100,000 years. Thinly dispersed matter cannot react to create visible light but when the same material becomes packed together light is produced in several ways. The mere compaction of atoms and molecules into confined space brings about increasing collisions, rising temperatures and eventually light. This may have been what happened early in the second creative period when the firmament, or center of the galaxy came into being. Depending on the mass involved a compacting body may or may not develop thermonuclear reactions. Only in bodies where the internal temperature exceeds 10,000,000 degrees Kelvin, can such energy-producing, matter-destroying reactions begin. When this stage is reached, self-luminous stars such as the sun are born. This may be what happened later in the sequence of creative periods.

How darkness might be produced in a cosmos dominated by light is a problem that must also be considered. The telescope proves that dark areas can be created but the processes involved remain mysterious. Scattered throughout the galaxy are many immense clouds of matter the compositions of which are only now becoming known. Some of these clouds are brightly illuminated by reactions of their constituent elements. Others are dimly lit by the light of scattered stars within them. Still others are utterly dark and so dense that no light from beyond can get through. Somehow these regions or aggregations of matter have become dark and isolated—in them the darkness has been divided from light on a local basis. Significantly enough these dark clouds are generally considered to be the birthplace of stars. Was it with some such aggregation that the creation of our system began? Possibilities multiply. Areas of intense and total darkness have clearly arisen within the galaxy. And just as surely these dark areas carry within them the material from which new and hotly blazing suns emerge. But, the actual birth of stars is again literally shrouded in obscurity. That new stars do appear quite suddenly is an established fact—their images are not on older photographic plates but are there now. Do they wink on, like street lights in groups or clusters, or one by one when conditions are right? Is the sudden blaze of nuclear fission preceded by a dull glow of radiation generated by compaction alone. Are there many bodies which fail by a thin margin to become self-luminous because they didn't reach the necessary size? Until such questions can be answered, it must suffice for purposes of building a coherent story to concede that there are ample possibilities for creating alternations of darkness and light that do not arise from motions of the earth as such.

According to the scriptural narrative on or by the fourth day the heavenly bodies as well as the earth were in existence—the sun and moon were there to give "light to the earth," and also to "divide the light from the darkness." This clearly means that by now a local sun-earth-moon system had been established and additional means of creating periods of alternating light and darkness were possible.

Consider the earth alone. Its constituents were most likely gathered together as cold particles, swirling in a lightless, murky cloud before the sun began to shine. At first the earth was probably a somewhat loose aggregation of fragments, not unlike certain comets are thought to be. The solid parts that may have ranged from dust to moon-like chunks of considerable size became glued, stuck or frozen together by various kinds of material including ices of water, carbon dioxide, methane and ammonia. Even tarry, carbonacious materials may have been present. This heterogeneous "popcorn ball" grew by gathering up whatever came within its gravitational influence over a rather long time period. The sweeping up process still isn't complete as shown by the fact that tons of meteorite material still fall into the earth's atmosphere each day.

No doubt the compacting effects of gravity soon began to take effect on the central regions of the earth-ball so that elements and compounds were forced together and began to react according to their chemical natures. All lines of evidence agree that the earth eventually melted completely, a reaction that seems not to have affected the moon or any of the other earth-like planets. Some thoughts as to why and how this happened are given in chapter 19. The point to be made here is that a molten earth would undoubtedly have been luminous just as molten lava is luminous. The over-all light may have been relatively weak and far less intense than that from thermonuclear reactions such as go on in the sun. But at any rate light had again been divided from darkness or a period of light had succeeded a period of darkness in the history of the system. This may have defined the fourth day of creation.

Obviously the earth did not remain molten—this stage of its existence may have been from about four and one-half billion to four billion years ago. It then passed from a light-producing body to a dark one and has remained so ever since. The earth and similar planets are "stars that failed" in one sense of the term. The next interval is difficult to reconstruct from the clues that are available. The history of the moon and the sun now concern us. The peculiar wording of the scriptures has meaning if properly understood. Consider:

> And I, God, made two great lights; the greater light to rule the day, and the lesser light to rule the night, and the greater light was the sun, and the lesser light was the moon;... And the sun to rule over the day, and the moon to rule over the night, and to divide the light from the darkness...."

There are more questions than answers at this point. Did the sun begin to shine on the fourth day after the earth had melted and cooled? At present scientists are divided in their opinion as to when the sun began to "rule the day." The same type of question applies to the beginning of light-generation by the sun and the appearance of this light on the planet earth. We need to be reminded that there probably was, at this stage, a great deal of unorganized material still swirling about the sun between and among the newly formed planets and their satellites. This might be considered as an early atmosphere of the sun and of the various planets. Again, everyday experience helps; a relatively small cloud layer can cut out the image of the sun, a thick thundercloud creates darkness almost as black as night. A volcanic eruption can bring on complete blackness. Imagine what clouds of matter 10 or 100 or 1000 times as thick as earthly clouds could do. The earth-moon system would have been in total darkness as long as these bodies were surrounded by or in a sense embedded in their own unorganized atmospheres.

We come briefly to the moon. After long debate it is fairly well agreed (1978) that it was formed from the same primitive dust cloud as the earth and did not come from a distant place or from the earth itself. The chemical differences between the earth and moon can be accounted for by their different sizes and slightly different evolutionary histories within a common mass of material. It is this final cloud that concerns us. It has obviously been swept away—we see the moon clearly; it now literally "rules the night" in complete visibility. Somewhere in the past the moon became visible but always by the "borrowed light" of the sun. Also, sometime in the past, the sun "broke through" and darkness was again divided from light or light replaced darkness in the history of the earth. This time it was truly the sun and the moon that divided the light from the darkness. Could this be the event that marks the fifth day?

At least one more division of light and dark had to come about and this final one resulted in the division of day and night as men usually understand them. This event was probably the beginning of the rotation of the earth on its axis. The question of just when the earth began to rotate may never be answered but we know it is now rotating very steadily and reliably. So does every other planet and every satellite of our system. The case of the moon is puzzling, its period of rotation is equal to its period of revolution—both about 27 days. Evidence is that the rotation of the earth was once more rapid, it is slowing down and the slowing down seems to be due to the gravitational action of the moon. Unfortunately space does not permit complete discussion of this and other interesting topics. Sufficient to say that the earth appears to have been rotating ever since it became a solid body and by its rotation every spot on its surface experiences an alternation of light and darkness or of day and night. Was this the final division, the one that introduces the sixth day?

Comments and References

The reality of alternating periods of light and darkness during the progressive history of the universe, galaxy, solar system, and earth may be verified by studying up-to-date material on cosmology, astronomy, and geology. References given in connection with other chapters are sufficient. However the successive periods of light and darkness must be carefully noted or it may not be apparent that they actually existed.

For comments by theological writers on the days of creation consult *The Interpreters Bible,* 1952, vol. 1, p. 468-491; *The Universal Jewish Encyclopedia* (1941 edition), vol. 3, p. 395; *The Encyclopedia of Biblical Interpretation* (Jewish), volume on Genesis 1, pp. 38-85; and *The New Catholic Encyclopedia,* vol. 4, pp. 423-424.

God Called the Light Day and the Darkness...Night 14

"And God called the light Day, and the darkness he called Night...."

Genesis 1:5

"And I, God, called the light Day; and the darkness, I called Night; and this I did by the word of my power,...."

Moses 2:5

"And the Gods called the light Day, and the darkness they called Night. And it came to pass that from the evening until morning they called night; and from the morning until the evening they called day; and this was the first, or the beginning, of that which they called day and night."

Abraham 4:5

Few things in earthly experience exceed in importance the successive alternations of light and darkness that men call days and nights. All human activity, individual as well as collective, is governed by the fact that such alterations occur. Sleep and wakefulness, activity and inactivity, rest and labor follow the pattern of day and night. We "count the days" before, between, and after events that are of importance to us. Other figures of speech such as our "days being numbered," or "days drawing to a close" are commonly used.

Early in life we are taught what it is that causes the days and nights. We learn about the revolution of the earth and its relation to the central sun. Every school child becomes aware of that which Copernicus struggled to comprehend and convey to his contemporaries. The day as we define it is arbitrarily divided into twenty-four hours and the ability to tell time by the clock is another vital piece of our youthful education. Small wonder that such hard-earned knowledge gives every informed person a rather definite concept of what is meant by the words day and night.

Common sense and a minimum of research should convince anyone, however, that God's Days and Nights cannot be the days and nights of human experience. The scriptural account is clear on this point. There could be no ordinary astronomical day-night relationships without a light-giving sun and no sun is mentioned until the fourth day of creation. It seems to have been the intent of God to commence the designation of creative days even while the earth was without form, certainly before the "firmament" of heaven was created.

These obvious scriptural facts should serve as a caution that the creative days were different from man's days. The scriptures leave no doubt as to the intended meaning—light is called Day, darkness is called Night. Only this and nothing more, no earth-sun relationships are described or required at this stage.

As the story unfolds this conclusion is verified: a succession of distinct "days" is described each with its particular events and products. That such division is more than a mere literary device or arbitrary convenience becomes evident when the facts and well-founded theories of astronomy are considered. This will be treated more fully in appropriate chapters that follow.

Comments and References

God's decision to call the light Day and the darkness Night as a method of time-keeping throughout the creation is not a matter needing scientific verification. A little thought and research will convince anyone that the relation of light and darkness to what we now call day and night is not the only possible arrangement. The people of the Old Testament had a different scheme, one that is still observed in the Jewish festivals and Sabbath observance. Comments on this ancient time-keeping method are found in *The Universal Jewish Encyclopedia* (1941 edition), p. 493; *The Interpreters Bible* (1952), vol. 1, pp. 470-471; and *The Catholic Dictionary of Theology* (1976), p. 138.

15

And the Evening and the Morning Were the First Day

"And God saw the light, that it was good and God divided the light from the darkness.

And God called the light Day, and the darkness he called Night. And the evening and the morning were the first day."

Genesis 1:4-5

"And I, God, saw the light; and that light was good. And I, God, divided the light from the darkness.

And I, God, called the light Day; and the darkness, I called Night; and this I did by the word of my power, and it was done as I spake; and the evening and the morning were the first day."

Moses 2:4-5

"And they (the Gods) comprehended the light, for it was bright; and they divided the light, or caused it to be divided, from the darkness.

And the Gods called the light Day, and the darkness they called Night. And it came to pass that from the evening until morning they called night; and from the morning until the evening they called day; and this was the first, or the beginning, of that which they called day and night."

Abraham 4:4-5

Without the more lengthy explanation of Abraham 4:4-5 as to what constitutes the first day of creation the corresponding verses of Genesis and Moses would be obscure if not incomprehensible. Strictly and literally speaking in modern English an evening and a morning do not make a day; they are the transitions from day to night and night to day respectively. Neither does the interval from evening to morning constitute the day; it is only half of a day in terms of elapsed time and in general experience it is the dark part of the day and would commonly be called night.

Fortunately the account in Abraham makes clear that the definition of a scriptural day of creation is not the same as that which prevails today. According to long-established usage— perhaps beginning initially with the making of reliable clocks the day commences at midnight and ends at midnight. Certainly this transition, taking place as it does while most people are sleeping, causes a minimum of confusion. The common designation AM (for ante-meridian) and PM (for post-meridian) tell us which side of midnight we are referring to. But every time zone has a different meridian of reference; this is so that the steady progression of light and darkness around the earth can be divided into 24 arbitrary steps that are more convenient for human use. There is, however, one master meridian to which all earthly time is referred. This meridian, passing through Greenwich, England, has its own progression of time like every other possible point but by common consent the time at this place becomes everyone's time—namely Greenwich time. Everyone who uses this standard knows what time it really is in one simple reference, he need not have a wall full of clocks.

The biblical day was established before clocks were invented and meridians established. It is based on the natural reoccurrence of light and darkness. The tradition of the Jewish religion preserves this ancient meaning. According to the Encyclopedia Judaica: "Sabbath and festivals begin in the evening and terminate at the start of the following night." This is also honored in the halakhic postulate that "the day goes after the night." God has employed this analogy throughout the creation scripture in describing the succession of events which are called nights and days.

Putting this interpretation to the test we must conclude that the first creative day began while there was yet light but darkness was approaching. God tells Moses, "I caused darkness to come up upon the face of the deep." The resulting darkness was the night of the first creative period. Then followed a period of light that concluded it. Under this interpretation we reach the somewhat surprising conclusion that the creation of heaven and earth mentioned in the first verse of Genesis should probably not be included in the six creative periods.

This agrees with what has been said in Chapter 8 on the topic of the appearance of darkness early in the creative accounts. In summary, the first day of creation, as God evidently intended the expression to be understood, began, not with the "big bang" of science but sometime after as its effects were dimming and a period of darkness was approaching. This is not to be interpreted that God had nothing to do with things before the six days of creation began. He created the heaven and the earth of Genesis 1:1 just as surely as he created anything else. One conclusion is that there was a long period of inaction, perhaps one might call it chaotic or disorganized, in the universe of space and matter before the Gods selected a part of it from which to construct an earth.

Comments and References

Scholars have pondered the meaning of the phrase "and the evening and the morning were the first day." That the same wording should also occur in connection with the second, third, fourth, and fifth days has been judged to be needless and unduly repetitious. Discussions up to this point should prove that in the creation scriptures no words are wasted or without meaning. The significance of designating each day as being the combination of a period of light and a period of darkness has been discussed in connection with chapters 13 and 14. The problem of this chapter is where in the history of the earth-system the first day of the scriptural account begins.

According to Jewish custom the day begins in the evening as light fades and darkness approaches. If this is truly symbolic of the creation, the first day also began as light faded and gave way to darkness. There is indeed such a transition and it is an essential one in the big-bang theory. A suitable place to commence enumeration of the creative days would seem to be when the brilliance of the original great fire-ball was fading away. The succeeding period of universal darkness would thus be the "evening" of the first day while the appearance and dominance of light in the galaxy we call our own would be the "morning" of the first day. As will be apparent in subsequent events this gets us off on the right count or combination of evening-morning or dark-light sequences.

This particular starting point bypasses but does not eliminate much that is important both scripturally and scientifically. The big-bang or initial creation of matter and space is not part of the first day. Likewise, there is nothing whatever to indicate what conditions were like before the big-bang. Most significant of all, the command "let there be light" did not initiate creation, it was uttered long after the heaven and earth of Verse 1 had been established.

16

The Firmament...Called...Heaven

"And God said, Let there be a firmament in the midst of the waters, and let it divide the waters from the waters.

And God made the firmament, and divided the waters which were under the firmament from the waters which were above the firmament: and it was so.

And God called the firmament Heaven. And the evening and the morning were the second day."

Genesis 1:6-8

"And again, I, God, said: Let there be a firmament in the midst of the water, and it was so, even as I spake; and I said: Let it divide the waters from the waters; and it was done;

And I, God, made the firmament and divided the waters, yea, the great waters under the firmament from the waters which were above the firmament, and it was so even as I spake.

And I, God, called the firmament Heaven; and the evening and the morning were the second day."

Moses 2:6-8

"And the Gods also said: Let there be an expanse in the midst of the waters, and it shall divide the waters from the waters.

And the Gods ordered the expanse, so that it divided the waters which were under the expanse from the waters which were above the expanse; and it was so, even as they ordered.

And the Gods called the expanse, Heaven. And it came to pass that it was from evening until morning that they called night; and it came to pass that it was from morning until evening that they called day; and this was the second time that they called night and day."

Abraham 4:6-8

Many problems arise in transforming the words of these verses into a concrete picture of the true relationships of heaven and earth. Much depends on how the word firmament is to be understood. Several definitions are available, one seems to offer the concept of wide open space with practically nothing in it, the other suggests something localized and solid. According to the Oxford English Dictionary, a respected authority in the origin of words, the term firmament in classical Latin means "something that strengthens and supports;" a near synonym is another word meaning a "firm or solid structure." The Hebrew word probably means "expanse" from the root *raqia.* However in Syrian the verb means "to condense, to make firm or solid." Building on these uncertain ancient roots and attempting to relate them to modern equivalent words and concepts has been difficult for translators. Usage seems to favor the idea that the firmament of Genesis is merely the arch or vault of the sky but the thought that it is also the place where God dwells is clearly permissible in theological contexts. The Oxford Dictionary concludes that in the strict and literal etymological sense a firmament is anything which strengthens or supports; a substratum, or a firm support or foundation.

A student of Genesis is apparently left to decide whether the firmament is below or above his head, whether it is solid or unsubstantial, and whether it is a specific place or the entirety of space. In choosing among these possibilities ancient thinkers came to what are obviously impossible or nonsense interpretations such as those illustrated in quaint Medieval drawings that show the earth as flat and the sky as a transparent hemisphere arching over it and the whole surrounded by water. The findings of astronomy and space exploration prove the impossibility of such reconstructions and it is difficult to believe that they were taught in all seriousness not many centuries ago. It must be realized that thinkers of those times also believed in a flat, immovable earth, in concentric crystalline heavenly spheres, and in the "windows of heaven" as literal truths.

Misinterpretations such as these surrounding Biblical references to the firmament have had the effect of creating doubt and distrust in the Creation scriptures generally. Critics and doubters, seemingly in the majority today, believe that Genesis merely puts into words the prevailing misconceptions of ancient times. Believers, on the other hand, are confident that the scriptures are inspired and must somehow be correct even though their correctness is difficult to prove.

As a first step toward reconciliation of modern fact and ancient scripture alternate interpretations of key words and concepts should be given a fair trial. Consider the word firmament was intended to designate the literal heaven, where God resides and that it is also a relatively firm and solid place as its ancient root-words clearly imply. This opens up a whole new line of thought which, if followed through to its conclusion, might well remove long-standing misunderstandings of this part of the scriptures.

Modern scriptures make it plain that God does reside in a specific place—a sphere as definite as the one which man inhabits. The explanation given by Joseph Smith which appears in the Pearl of Great Price under the title, A Facsimilie from the Book of Abraham No. 2 contains a number of astronomical notations:

> Fig. 1. Kolob, signifying the first creation, nearest the celestial, or the residence of God. First in government, the last pertaining to the measurement of time.... One day in Kolob is equal to a thousand years according to the measurement of this earth....
>
> Fig. 2. Stands next to Kolob, called by the Egyptians Oliblish, which is the next grand governing creation near to the celestial or the place where God resides....

Also, in the Book of Abraham it is written:

> "And I, Abraham, had the Urim and Thummim, which the Lord my God had given unto me, in Ur of the Chaldees:
>
> And I saw the stars that they were very great, and that one of them was nearest unto the throne of God; and there were many great ones which were near unto it;
>
> And the Lord said unto me: These are the governing ones; and the name of the great one is Kolob, because it is near unto me, for I am the Lord thy God: I have set this one to govern all those which belong to the same order as that upon which thou standest."
>
> Abraham 3:1-3

The place where God resides is not named as a separate body in this revelation. There can be no doubt that it is a body or globe however. Conditions there are described at least in part in other scriptures.

> "The angels do not reside on a planet like this earth;
> But they reside in the presence of God, on a *globe* like
> a sea of glass and fire, where all things for their glory are

manifest, past, present, and future, and are continually before the Lord.

The place where God resides is a great Urim and Thummim."

D & C 130:6-8

Also:

"...The heavens is a place where God dwells and all his holy angels."

Alma 18:30

Man was created in heaven by God:

"...For I, the Lord God, created all things, of which I have spoken, spiritually, before they were naturally upon the face of the earth.... And I, the Lord God, had created all the children of men; and not yet a man to till the ground; *for in heaven created I them;...*"

Moses 3:5

Is it possible to learn anything from science that correlates with the scriptural words regarding the location of heaven? We are told that it (heaven) is near the great star Kolob and Kolob is one of the governing bodies of the order (system?) in which man resides. Man's residence is the planet Earth and it belongs to a number of systems. There is an earth-moon system, a solar system and a galactic system. But there are also other families, orders or systems of bodies that include the earth. There are families or groups of stars like the sun—the Pleidaes and Ursa Major (Big Dipper) constitute such groupings. Star groups like this apparently form simultaneously from the same cloud of matter.

It is well-known that the Milky Way Galaxy is part of a system of galaxies called the Local Group. This group consists of our galaxy, the two Magellanic Clouds, the great Andromeda galaxy and some two dozen other members. Progressing still higher among astronomical orders we find giant clusters of many galaxies. To such aggregations the name supergalaxy is applied. Some of these are enormous by any standard, one cluster in the constellation Coma Bernices is made up of about 10,000 galaxies. One writer has posed the question, "And would there not be clusters of supergalaxies and clusters of clusters of supergalaxies and so on?" This is a profound question but one that might well be answered in the affirmative.

What is the message of the scripture which reads:

"Now, if there be two things, one above the other, and the moon above the earth, then it may be that a planet or a star may exist above it; and there is nothing that the Lord thy God shall take in his heart to do but what he will do it."

Abraham 3:17

For the time being the design of the universe is a matter of intense study. How much we may learn is not evident. As God informed Moses there is much that remains with him that may or may not be revealed to mortal man.

Comments and References

The creation of the Firmament is clearly a very essential step in God's creative work. Attempts to understand and describe what the Firmament is have always been hopelessly entangled with the naive impossible ideas about the structure of the cosmos that prevailed in ancient times. Modern scholars do not agree as to whether Genesis puts into words the essence of older beliefs or if it, being older, is the ultimate source of these beliefs. What scholars imagine the author(s) of Genesis had in mind is amply illustrated by discussions in *The Interpreters Bible,* p. 472; *The Catholic Biblical Encyclopedia,* p. 367-368; *The New Catholic Encyclopedia,* vol. 5, p. 935, and *The Encyclopedia of Biblical Interpretation* (Jewish), vol. on Genesis I.

Events that led to the irrevocable decline and abandonment of ancient and medieval ideas about the cosmos are well described in Stephen Toulmin and Jane Goodfield, 1965, *The Discovery of Time,* Harper and Row; same authors, 1961, *The Fabric of the Heavens,* Harper; J. C. Greene, 1959, *The Death of Adam,* Mentor Books; Arthur Koestler, 1959, *The Sleepwalkers,* Grosset and Dunlap; and C. G. Gillispie, 1959, *Genesis and Geology,* Harper.

Although modern scholars may understand perfectly well what pre-scientific peoples imagined about the Firmament, neither ancient nor modern thinkers have examined all possible meanings. Modern discoveries clearly justify the thought that the Firmament is the center or hub of a galaxy such as our own Milky Way.

Studies of galaxies is a foremost field of modern astronomy. Informative books include: Harlow Shapley, 1960, *Galaxies,* Holt, Rinehart and Winston; Bart Bok and Priscilla Bok, 1974, *The Milky Way,* Harvard University Press; Lloyd Motz, 1976, *The Universe: Its*

Beginning and End, Schribner; Simon Mitton, 1977, *Exploring the Galaxies,* Schribner; W. J. Kaufman III, 1977, *Astronomy, the Structure of the Universe,* Macmillan; W. Becker and G. Contopoulos (eds.), 1970, *The Spiral Structure of Our Galaxy,* Springer-Verlag.

Specific articles emphasizing the structure of the central area of our galaxy and what goes on there are: Bart J. Bok, 1972, Updating galactic spiral structure: *American Scientist,* vol. 60, pp. 709-722; Gerrit L. Verschuur, 1976, Infrared Astronomy: *Astronomy,* March, 1976.

17 Waters...Under the Firmament... Above the Firmament

"And God made the firmament, and divided the waters which were under the firmament from the waters which were above the firmament: and it was so."

Genesis 1:7

"And I, God, made the firmament and divided the waters, yea, the great waters under the firmament from the waters which were above the firmament, and it was so even as I spake."

Moses 2:7

"And the Gods ordered the expanse, so that it divided the waters which were under the expanse from the waters which were above the expanse; and it was so, even as they ordered."

Abraham 4:7

God called the firmament Heaven and Heaven is where he resides. These are scriptural verities. The location of Heaven, although not explicitly stated, is almost surely the center of our galaxy. The critical scripture is from the Book of Abraham:

"And I saw the stars, that they were very great, and that one of them was nearest unto the throne of God; and there were many great ones which were near unto it;

And the Lord said unto me: These are the governing ones; and the name of the great one is Kolob, because it is near unto me, for I am the Lord thy God: I have set this one to govern all those which belong to the same order as that upon which thou standest."

Abraham 3:2-3

There are several possible interpretations of the word "order" as it appears in this revelation. One obvious astronomical order to which the earth belongs is the solar system. But Kolob is obviously not the Sun; the Sun has its own name, Shinehah (Abraham 3:13). The galaxy is a much greater order embracing the earth, sun and countless other bodies. It has a center or core around which all these revolve. What is known about the center of the galaxy need not be discussed here. Sufficient to say that a scientific description confirms Abraham's and lends great credibility to the conclusion that Kolob and hence Heaven is at the center of our Milky Way Galaxy.

Assuming that Heaven is at or near the center of the galaxy what is to be understood by the reference to waters under the firmament and waters above the firmament? Being earth-bound creatures we immediately think in earth-bound terms. Above is anything lying upward from the surface or center of the earth. Below is downward toward the surface or center of the earth. We usually accept the surface of the earth or our own position on it as a reference when we think of anything being under or above. It is simply upward or downward from the surface or ourselves on the surface. Gravity, ever with us, helps tell what is up and down and thus above or below us.

Our earth-bound frame of reference is obviously of great use in everyday thinking but of no use when we move away from the earth. In absolute rather than relative terms what is down to the inhabitants of Salt Lake City is up to those of Brisbane, Australia.

As I write this I have before me one of the famous space photos of the Earth, taken by the Apollo astronauts. Here is the earth hanging in space against a background of uniform darkness—nothing else visible. I search the globe for landmarks for there are patches of land showing through the cover of swirling clouds. I locate part of the familiar coastlines of Africa because the ruddy desert here contrasts with the dark oceans and there are fewer clouds over the land. Then I automatically shift the photo so that north is up in my view. Now I can see other outlines—I have become oriented. I have adjusted my view to a frame of reference without really thinking how that frame of reference came into being and what it means when we are on the earth or far from it in distant space.

The astronauts found, when far from earth and its gravity field that familiar terms such as up and down, below and above, north and south became meaningless. Only when they decided on some celestial object as a reference point could they even describe their surroundings. This is the problem astronomers have had to solve in an arbitrary way as they map and describe the heavens. They have solved the problem by projecting the system used on earth into the celestial sphere. Thus the north celestial pole is a point in the heavens toward which the north pole of the earth is pointing. There is also a celestial equator that hangs directly over the terrestrial one. The earth and sky are like two great globes, the former inside the later and both divisible in terms of latitude and longitude, into degrees, minutes and seconds. Just as a remote spot in the ocean can be located by this grid system so can the faintest star in heaven be pin-pointed on the celestial sphere.

Certainly it was a natural tendency or even necessity of thinking in earth-bound terms that led to earlier interpretations of the scriptures under discussion. There are many ancient and medieval illustrations that purport to show waters above the earth (clouds, rain, etc.) and waters below the earth (in subterranean caves and reservoirs).

The obvious impossibility of these interpretations, as proved by space exploration and by a better understanding of the structure of the earth is one reason why literal interpretations of the scripture have fallen into disrepute. But the scriptures may be strengthened, not weakened, by alternate choices of a few key words and phrases. The waters above and under the firmament are not the waters of the earth, they are the waters of space already described in chapter 11.

May we return briefly for a moment to the thought that the firmament (Heaven) is in the center of the galaxy and consider how the structure of this great system might be described in a simple understandable way? Our galaxy is not unusual, there are other examples by the thousands making up the class of galaxies that have two curving spiral arms lying in one plane. The discovery that we live in a spiral galaxy is one of the triumphs of modern astronomy.

Since galactic arms occur almost without exception in opposite, identical, and symmetrical pairs they might be distinguished by comparing their locations with respect to their common center of rotation. Thus they could be identified as being right and left, to the north or south, up and down or above and below. On the face of it one choice appears to be as good as another. In the scripture the problem of describing the galaxy is solved neatly enough by referring to one of the arms as being *above* the firmament, the other *under* the firmament. This scheme makes it possible to specify the location of the matter and space that would later become the solar system and the earth.

Comments and References

The most abundant type of galaxy has a spiral shape with two symmetrically coiling arms springing from opposite sides of a central hub or bulge. The purpose of this chapter is to draw attention to the fact that Genesis 1:7 can be interpreted in terms of this typical configuration.

Galactic structure is one of the major mysteries of astronomy. The over-all shape of a spiral galaxy suggests that the center is rotating at a relatively rapid rate and that material composing the arms is lagging or streaming behind. While it is true that spiral galaxies do rotate this is clearly not the full explanation of the arms and their variations. Many books and articles discuss the problems of galactic structure and motion: W. Becker and G. Contopoulos (eds.), 1970, *The Spiral Structure of Our Galaxy,* International Astronomical Union Symposium, No. 38, Springer-Verlag; Gerrit L. Verschour and Kenneth I. Kellermann (eds.), *Galactic and Extra-Galactic Radio Astronomy,* Springer-Verlag; Bart J. Bok, 1972, *Updating Galactic Spiral Structure,* in American Scientist, vol. 60, pp. 709-722; Richard B. Larsen, 1977, *The Origin of Galaxies,* in American Scientist, vol. 65, No. 2.

Interesting as the subject of the origin and shape of galaxies may be it need not be intensively studied or thoroughly understood in order to judge the possible significance of interpreting this part of Genesis on the basis of galactic shapes alone.

18 Gathered Together Unto One Place

"And God said, Let the waters under the heaven be gathered together unto one place, and let the dry land appear: and it was so."

Genesis 1:9

"And I, God, said: Let the waters under the heaven be gathered together unto one place, and it was so; and I, God, said: Let there be dry land; and it was so."

Moses 2:9

"And the Gods ordered, saying: Let the waters under the heaven be gathered together unto one place, and let the earth come up dry; and it was so as they ordered;"

Abraham 4:9

The gathering of waters into one place, which is the topic of this chapter, is an essential step in the preparation of the earth. However, this step is logical and right only if the major conclusions of previous chapters are acceptable. One essential premise is that the waters referred to are not the water bodies of the planet Earth but are instead the unorganized material of interstellar space, portions of which are very rich in water as such. A second premise is that the waters under the firmament and the waters above the firmament refer to the two opposite spiral arms of the galaxy.

Building on the assumption that these conclusions are basically correct the next step follows logically. Note the expression waters *under* the heavens, not the waters *above* the heavens. This wording neatly makes known that the scene of action is being restricted to a specific area of space, namely one part of a two-part system. What goes on across space in the opposite arm of the galaxy no longer enters the picture.

Further restrictions become evident. Although it might be inferred from the brief wording of the text that *all* the waters in one arm of the galaxy were gathered into one place this is not necessarily so. A very small part of the original cloud suffices to produce an entire solar system. One thing that seems to exist in overwhelming sufficiency is matter. The text does not specify that the segregated material was to become the earth only. In its initial form the original "gathering" may have been material of the entire solar system, or even a local system of a number of stars. The emphasis is on a process that would eventually give rise to the earth.

The whole process of formation and evolution of astronomical bodies of all magnitudes from groups of galaxies through single galaxies, star groups, individual stars, planets and satellites may be thought of in terms of successive accretions or "gatherings." Astronomers recognize different processes which might be included in the comprehensive term gathering. These are mostly self-explanatory; gravitational attraction, accretion, and condensation. The process was ongoing and very complex. The material for the galaxies had to be segregated early in the history of the universe; this was followed by condensations within the galaxies which were destined to become individual star systems or groups of related stars. Still later the material of the stellar systems underwent condensations so that individual stars, binary twins or complex planetary systems were produced. Finally, many planets show the effects of continuing accretionary processes whereby their satellite systems came into being. For example, the Earth and Moon are thought to have formed from the same dust and gas cloud. Jupiter and Saturn with their satellites are miniature solar systems each having formed from its separate cloud.

An interesting description of the final gathering together of earth materials appears in an excellent book *Planetary Geology* by Nicholas M. Short.

"Details of the processes by which the planets grew from the solar nebula are still inferential. Clots of matter probably built up into tiny planetesimals held together by frozen ammonia, or water, organic matter, and magnetic or electrical charges. The initial aggregation may have resulted from random collisions in turbulent vortices in the cloud or from faster-moving particles overtaking slower ones in the path-crossing elliptical orbits that prevailed in the rotating disc. At first the planetesimals were probably only meters in size but as individuals reached critical mases they began to have significant gravitational effects on their neighbors and thus attracted smaller particles into themselves. Growth rates increased with time—the initial clots formed in less than 100,000 years; asteroidal-sized bodies took no more than 10 million years; the entire planetary system reached its present dimensions in less than 100 million years. Eventually, the larger bodies, growing at the expense of the smaller ones, swept up so much of the remaining materials that only a few planet-sized aggregates were left." (pp. 51-52)

The history of each aggregation regardless of its size or present relationships began when its component materials were "gathered in one place." Before its separation each entity was a part of something larger, afterward it had its own individuality. Nothing significant appears to be added or subtracted to most astronomical bodies once their basic materials are separated from the constituents that are destined to become other bodies. Astronomical birth is like the birth of an organism—it is the event which separates offspring from parent and starts it on a separate course. Each entity has a time of birth and it is from this moment that its history and the calculation of its age begins. It is the nature of the universe that galaxies, suns, and even planets must run their separate courses mostly in solitary isolation. There may be reactions between bodies across the reaches of space it is true but exchange of material is practically non-existent. The importance of space is verified by the scriptural reference from Abraham "...We will go down, for there is space there, and we will take of these materials, and we will make an earth whereon these may dwell;" (Abraham 3:24.)

Observation teaches that astronomical bodies of all types evolve and change after their segregation. That which commences as a disorganized mass of gas and dust may condense into a much smaller space to become a galaxy; lightless and shapeless clumps of matter within galaxies in turn become self-luminous stars; rotating disks of gas and dust attending newly formed stars are segregated into the rings or clouds destined to become planets or satellites. Wandering remnants may condense to asteroids or comets or remain as grains of dust. What an object contains and its location at the time it begins its separate existence largely determines what it ultimately becomes. Although all essential elements are in each shapeless unorganized cloud at its beginning, the final product will not emerge until much later. Nevertheless, under the operation of law, the final outcome is largely predetermined by what originally enters into each packet of matter.

The theme of Genesis 1:9 is clearly the emergence of a solid planet from formerly diffuse unorganized material. The formation of the earth has always been a topic of great interest to geologists and astronomers and one to which they have devoted a great deal of attention. After all, we do have the end product, the solid earth, for first-hand study and are rapidly gleaning from other nearby astronomical bodies information that is important to understanding the origin of our home planet. A very brief synopsis of the history of theories of the origin of the solar system may not be out of place.

The first serious attempt to explain the origin of the solar system was in 1644 when the French philosopher Rene Descartes proposed that it all began as a cloud of unorganized primordial matter. The sun and planets, he believed, were formed from great eddies or swirls within the initial cloud. In 1755 Immanual Kant elaborated and refined the nebular theory by taking into account the laws of gravity that had been propounded by Newton in 1687. Kant, by combining the idea of spiral motion and gravitational attraction, came up with a surprisingly good model for the origin of the solar system.

Other theories of the solar system have been proposed over the centuries but none of any consequence commences with anything basically different from the nebulous aggregation of matter visualized by Descartes. How the original material passed from its diffuse condition as gas and dust to large solid bodies has always been the greatest problem.

To achieve the successively more dense aggregations that constitute the sun, planets and satellites it is necessary to visualize various processes whereby portions of matter are separated or gathered out of larger masses. It is with regard to the segregating processes that the various Nebular Theories differ from each other. As chemistry and physics have provided more sophisticated understanding of the laws governing such processes the successive theories have clearly become more satisfactory and believable.

For larger entities at least, gravity seems entirely able to accomplish the drawing together and compression of matter that resulted in the solar system. Some theories would produce the sun first and then the planets while others would produce the planets first and the sun later. Even so, both classes of theories begin with a mass of dust and gas which has already undergone condensation and commenced to rotate about its center of gravity. One view is that essentially all the original material became concentrated in a single central sun or star. According to the law of conservation of angular momentum the speed of rotation increases as the material is drawn together in such a body. Speed of rotation is the critical factor of this theory for it is the excessive speed of the central contracting sun which is supposed to give rise to the planets. It is known on theoretical grounds that when the speed of a liquid body reaches a certain limit, it will begin to spill out or lose material from the most rapidly rotating equatorial zone. This will take the form of a thin ring or rings somewhat resembling the rings of Saturn. It is from this material spilled out of the sun that the planets, according to the theory, are derived. Enough rings, each of somewhat different composition, are supposed to have been produced to form the separate planets. By complex systems of eddies and currents the material of each ring was subsequently condensed into its respective planet. A great difficulty with this theory is that the central sun is now rotating far too slowly to give off rings and there is little evidence that it ever had the necessary velocity to do so in the past.

Theories of a second class are more popular today and seem to satisfy more of the known facts. Again the initial material is a diffuse, flattened, slowly rotating cloud of dust and gas. As the material draws together, irregular clouds or knots of material are left behind while the greater bulk continues to spiral slowly inward. It is the material left behind that becomes the planets. An attractive feature of this theory is that it explains why there are two distinct groups of planets and why each planet is different from the others. Members of the outer group, Jupiter, Saturn, Uranus and Neptune are larger, mostly gaseous and have large numbers of satellites. The inner group, Mercury, Venus, Earth and Mars—are small, dense, heavy and have few satellites.

According to this theory the material for the outer larger, gaseous planets was left behind before the sun came into existence as the governing central body. These giant outer planets may, in fact, have approximately the composition of the parent nebula at the time they became separated from it. Now that spacecraft have passed near Jupiter and have obtained much data as to its structure and composition we are able to make more reliable comparisons with the Earth and the distant outer planets.

It is supposed that some time between the detachment of the material of Jupiter and that of the inner planets the sun became a self-luminous body in the center of the system. By this is meant that the central material had become so tightly packed and dense that nuclear reactions began. When a temperature of $10,000,000^{\circ}$ C. is reached, light and other radiation is produced and a shining star results. From this stage onward the sun would have dominated the formation and history of planets. The solar wind was increasingly important. This is the outward-pressing stream of light and other radiation which exerts a measurable pressure upon anything it encounters. The tails of comets are good examples of its effects. It is thought possible that the solar wind was effective in dispersing or sweeping away the lighter gaseous molecules near the sun so as to leave behind relatively more of the heavier elements such as silicon and iron. It is an abundance of these elements which characterizes the inner planets. By contrast the outer gaseous planets are rich in hydrogen and helium.

The present system is thought to have been in existence for almost 5 billion years during which time the sun has not only driven away much of its surrounding atmospheric cloud but also has burned away a great deal of its own substance. In earlier stages, the burning was very energetic and the sun was much hotter and brighter than it is now. The burning process literally "cleaned up" the solar system by sweeping away the remnants of the nebular cloud. This was the final event which brought the planet earth into existence as a separate solid body. The earth had at length "come up dry."

Comments and References

The ninth verse of Genesis I seems to be the first scripture pertaining specifically to the Solar System and Planet Earth. The modern view is that the Earth emerged as a culmination of successive gatherings or condensations. The processes by which the materials of galaxies is segregated from a universal cloud, how the solar nebula condensed within the Milky Way Galaxy and how the sun and planets gathered from the solar nebula are subjects of intense inquiry and speculation.

Books that deal with the problem of segregation or condensation include T. De Jong and M. Maedor, 1977, *Star Formation,* International Astronomical Union Symposium, No. 75, R. Reidel Publishing Co.; Clark R. Chapman, 1977, *The Inner Planets,* Scribner; C. G. Walker, 1977, *Origin of the Atmosphere,* Macmillan; Robert Jastrow and A. G. Cameron, 1963, *Origin of the Solar System,* Academic Press.

An entire issue of Scientific American, September 1975, vol. 33, No. 3 is devoted to the solar system. This is a readable, and well illustrated introduction to the system to which Earth belongs. Another excellent source is *New Frontiers in Astronomy,* a compilation of articles from the Scientific American, with an introduction by Owen Gingerich, 1975. Another selection of Scientific American papers is *Planet Earth,* Freeman, 1974. Bibliographies

of these sources open up practically all aspects of modern astronomy and earth science.

Let the Dry Land (Earth) Appear 19

"And God said, Let the waters under the heaven be gathered together unto one place, and let the dry land appear: and it was so. And God called the dry land Earth;..."

Genesis 1:9-10

"And I, God, said: Let the waters under the heaven be gathered together unto one place, and it was so; and I, God, said: Let there be dry land; and it was so.
And I, God, called the dry land Earth;..."

Moses 2:9-10

"And the Gods ordered, saying: Let the waters under the heaven be gathered together unto one place, and let the earth come up dry; and it was so as they ordered;
And the Gods pronounced the dry land, earth;..."

Abraham 4:9-10

The time-honored interpretation of the above passages is that they describe the creation of the major land and water features of the planet Earth. A special point is made of the "waters" being gathered unto one place. The picture of a single great continent emerging from the waters of the ocean is entirely compatible with the early earth-bound concept of creation. But there are several good reasons to question the assumption that the scriptural passages referred to apply to features of the planet Earth. As argued in chapters 11 and 12 it is more probable that the word "waters" designates the primitive mixture of elemental matter from which the various astronomical bodies, including the planet Earth, emerged. These arguments need not be repeated here. We turn to the manner in which the term earth is used in Genesis 1. Why is the dry land called Earth (capitalized) in verse 10 of both Genesis and Moses while in previous verses it is not capitalized? Both the capitalized

115

and uncapitalized form seem to come from the same Greek word, erets.

If there is any verse of Genesis which seems to refer specifically to the planet it is verse 10. If the capitalized term "Earth" is indeed the entire planet, then the "dry land" referred to in verse 9 must also be the same because God himself "called the dry land Earth." There is the distinct impression that God is here giving a name to the planet and not to the materials of which it is composed.

The scriptures are not without other references which bear on this problem. In his vision of creation Moses beheld many lands and "each land was called earth." Again two interpretations are possible. Each of the "lands" seen by Moses may have been a continent or island of the planet Earth or each may have been a separate planet somewhere in space. Reading on in the introductory chapter of Moses we find other possible clues. Moses pled for further enlightenment asking God "why these things are so, and by what thou madest them." The question apparently applies to more than just the planet Earth and God's reply would seem to leave no other interpretation: "And worlds without number have I created,..." (verse 33). Also, "But only an account of this earth, and the inhabitants thereof, give I unto you" (verse 35). Clearly God is making a distinction between this "earth" and other "worlds," not between the particular spot where Moses stood and other dry land areas of the Earth. Consider the continuation of verse 35, "For behold there are many worlds that have passed away by the word of my power. And there are many that now stand, and innumerable are they unto man...." Does this read like a reference to the inhabited parts of this Earth or to the other habitable planets of the universe. Which of these entities are truly innumerable or without number to man?

There are other arguments in favor of the thought that the earth or dry land referred to in the scripture is the entire globe and not the superficial land masses on its surface. If all the waters of the planet earth were in one place, they would constitute an ocean much larger than the Pacific. It is difficult to conceive of such an extensive sheet or shell of water as being "in one place" as it would have to encircle a large part of the earth. A field of alfalfa is not in one place as much as is a haystack.

If there is any doubt that God had in mind earths other than this one, the succeeding narrative should remove all doubt. Moses plead with God: "...Be merciful unto thy servant, O God, and tell me concerning this earth, and the inhabitants thereof, and also the heavens, and then thy servant will be content. And the Lord God spake unto Moses saying: the heavens, they are many, and they cannot be numbered unto man;... And as one earth shall pass away, and the heavens thereof even so shall another come;... I will speak unto thee concerning this earth upon which thou standest;..." (Moses 1:36-40.)

The concept of innumerable earths, or worlds each with its inhabitants was clearly revealed to Moses but is not recorded in Genesis probably because God did not permit Moses to pass along anything not pertaining to this particular planet and its creation. The wisdom of this restriction remained with God until the facts of other inhabited worlds were revealed or re-revealed to this generation. Consider not only the revelations in the Book of Moses:1 but also the following from the Doctrine and Covenants:

"And now, after the many testimonies which have been given of him, this is the testimony last of all, which we give of him, that he lives;

For we saw him, even on the right hand of God, and we heard the voice bearing record that he is the Only Begotten of the Father—

That by him and through him, and of him the worlds are and were created, and the inhabitants thereof are begotten sons and daughters unto God."

D & C 76:22-24

May we now attempt a new interpretation of the verses which tell of the appearance of the dry land or earth? Assume that what is being described is the formation of the solar system and the earth, not the shaping of continents and oceans. We are told that God ordered the waters under heaven to be gathered *unto one place*. As an alternate thought the coming together of the material that would in time become the solar system is also well described as a gathering. We have already made the point that "the waters under the heavens" probably refer to certain material in our arm of the galaxy. We follow good astronomical theory in visualizing the beginning of the solar system as a gathering together of some of the material in this arm. The scriptural language may be interpreted to mean that *all* the water under the heavens were gathered together in one place, but that only part of the material was thus localized is not ruled out. In any event the gathering together "in one place" seems to be a very acceptable description of the accumulation of matter in specific regions of space that was an essential step in the formation of a solar system and also in the formation of individual planets and satellites.

Thus we come at length to the undoubted references to the planet Earth. In this connection there is a significant difference in the wording between Abraham 4:9 and Genesis 1:9 which describe the event. Abraham reads: "...let the earth come up dry;..." Genesis reads: "...let the dry land appear:...." Following the wording of Abraham it is not difficult to visualize the planet emerging from enclosing mists or clouds. The wording of Genesis may not rule out such an interpretation but admittedly does not encourage it. No matter, the references to dry land or dry earth is scientifically very significant. The use of this wording forces the conclusion that the earth was at one stage without surface bodies of liquid water. If anyone has lingering doubts about the thought of a dry earth he should consider the opening event of the 7th day where the statement is made that there had been no rain up to that time. Admittedly there could be oceans without rain but such an arrangement raises additional problems that do not exist if there were no oceans.

Now that we know a great deal about other planets that are our neighbors in space we perceive that the existence of a watery planet is unusual. The Moon is now waterless and apparently always has been. Mercury shows no evidence of water whatsoever. The water on Mars at the present time is locked within the surface material, frozen in ice, or vaporized in the atmosphere. Venus appears too hot to support surface water or ice. Currently no one believes that there is enough water as such on any of these planets to greatly affect what goes on there and certainly not enough to support higher forms of life. One of the terms descriptive of these bodies is that they are *dry.* Furthermore, judging by the examples we have, it is more likely that a planet will "come up dry" than that it will emerge supplied with bodies of surface water.

Putting off for the time being a discussion of how the earth received its presently bounteous supply of surface water it is interesting to consider why it must have been dry at the beginning. There are several possible explanations; water may not have been available as such among the components that were then existing on or within the planet; water may have been in existence but only in frozen or gaseous form; water may have been lost or driven off by excessive heat derived either from the earth or from the sun. Evidence that the earth passed through a molten stage favors the last named explanation.

The best evidence for such a molten phase is the fact that the earth consists of a series of great shells or spheres arranged according to density. In other words the heavier material is found in the very dense core of iron and nickle or heavier metals; this is overlain by the mantle composed of iron, magnesium and silicon averaging six to eleven times as heavy as water; the outer shell of the solid earth, commonly called the crust, has an average density two to three times that of water; resting on the solid earth is the watery shell or hydrosphere and above this the various atmospheric levels ranging from dense to very light outward. The most logical explanation for this layered arrangement is that there must have been a time when heavy constituents of a complex original mixture could sink and light materials could rise freely to assume a position of equilibrium. The separation of milk and cream furnishes a simple analogy.

It should be stated that not all earth scientists and astronomers agree in the necessity of a molten earth. Some believe that the layered arrangement is an original feature—the heavier material was gathered from space first, the successively lighter constituents being added as time went on. At no time was there complete melting and mixing. The truth may lie somewhere between the ideas of a completely cold beginning and a completely hot one. No one doubts that the outer part of the core of the earth is now molten. Is it in process of cooling or in process of heating? No other planet appears to have a molten core such as the earth. This is based on the fact that the magnetic and electrical fields of the earth are much stronger than those of any other solid body so far investigated.

It is also known that a very hot plastic zone exists within the upper part of the earth's mantle from about 100 to 400 miles beneath the surface. This is called the asthenosphere and it is considered to be the source of much if not most of the volcanic material that appears at the surface. The upper solid layer, or lithosphere, rests very uneasily upon the plastic material and in fact slides about upon it to create vast earth movements that are continually altering the major surface features. Strangest of all is the discovery that the outer shell is being engulfed into the plastic layer and gradually destroyed along certain geologically active zones. This whole topic of what goes on at the surface and near the surface of the earth is an intensely interesting one that we cannot discuss here. Many good references are available.

The important point is that the earth is partly molten at the present time and has apparently been so for many geologic ages. No other planet has such an active history and except for Mars there is little evidence for much internal heat being generated or displayed by volcanic action. The landscapes of the other planets are very ancient and have remained unchanged since their formation. The surface of the earth, by contrast, is continually being altered and reorganized.

In the minds of most geologists the earth is what it is—active and changing because of the heat energy it generates and contains. This same heat energy may have been much greater in the past and would then have been sufficient to either prevent the accumulation of water or to drive off any that might have been present on the surface. In order to escape the gravitational pull of the earth a water molecule would have to possess a store of energy sufficient to give an average velocity of 11.2 kilometers per second. This is well within that which would be imparted by the temperature that would exist if the surface of the globe were molten lava which ranges between 700° C. and 1200° C.

One more agent may have been at work to create an originally "dry" earth. This is the so-called solar wind or radiation pressure. As the name suggests a force is exerted by the stream of powerful radiation (including light) that arises from the sun. The combination of rays and particles is sufficiently powerful to actually push molecules and small particles away from the sun. This incidentally, is the force which shapes and directs the outward streaming tails of comets as they enter the central regions of the solar system. During the earlier history of the system there is good reason to believe that the sun was hotter and more powerful in every way. At this time the solar wind could well have been sufficient to strip away and disperse all the lighter molecules, including water, that were produced from within or were attached by gravity to the earth.

Scriptures do not specify that the earth was originally either hot or cold. That it had to be hot in order to be dry is no great obstacle to interpreting the scripture. The important part is that it "came up dry." Later as both science and scripture affirm water appeared to make it what it is—a habitation for all life, including man.

Comments and References

This chapter describes the emergence of the Earth as a separate planet. Its appearance was essentially the final gathering together of the elements that would henceforth be separate and apart from other aggregations. In the broad sense the origin of the earth was merely an incident in the ongoing development of the solar system and it is impossible to think of its early history except in connection with the parent sun and sister plants.

The history of the solar system and early earth is discussed in most textbooks of geology and planetology. A suggested reference that traces the pre-planetary origins of the earth is W. L. Stokes,

1973, *Essentials of Earth History,* 3rd ed., Prentice-Hall. A compilation of many excellent papers from the Scientific American is *Planet Earth,* W. H. Freeman, 1974. An entire issue of Scientific American, September 1975, is devoted to the solar system and its origin.

The solid earth cannot be discussed without reference to the atmosphere and oceans that envelop it. Books that bear on the origin of the total planetary system are: James C. G. Walker, 1977, *Evolution of the Atmosphere,* Macmillan; Peter J. Brancazio, 1964, *The Origin and Evolution of Atmospheres and Oceans,* Wiley; and Jobert Jastrow and A. G. Cameron, 1963, *Origin of the Solar System,* Academic Press.

Other books and articles deal with more specific topics: V. S. Safronov, 1972, *Evolution of the Proplanetary Cloud and Formation of the Earth and Planets,* Israel Program for Scientific Translations, Jerusalem; Hubert Reeves, ed. 1972, *Symposium on the Origin of the Solar System,* Edition du Centre National de la Recherche Scientifique, Paris; Lawrence Grossman and John W. Larimer; 1974, *Chemical History of the Solar System,* in Reviews of Geophysics and Space Physics, vol. 12, No. 1.

20 Grass...Herb...Tree... The Third Day

"And God said, Let the earth bring forth grass, the herb yielding seed, and the fruit tree yielding fruit after his kind, whose seed is in itself, upon the earth: and it was so.

And the earth brought forth grass, and herb yielding seed after his kind, and the tree yielding fruit, whose seed was in itself, after his kind: and God saw that it was good.

And the evening and the morning were the third day."

Genesis 1:11-13

"And I, God, said: Let the earth bring forth grass, the herb yielding seed, the fruit tree yielding fruit, after his kind, and the tree yielding fruit, whose seed should be in itself upon the earth, and it was so even as I spake.

And the earth brought forth grass, every herb yielding seed after his kind, and the tree yielding fruit, whose seed should be in itself, after his kind; and I, God, saw that all things which I had made were good;

And the evening and the morning were the third day."

Moses 2:11-13

"And the Gods said: Let us prepare the earth to bring forth grass; the herb yielding seed; the fruit tree yielding fruit, after his kind, whose seed in itself yieldeth its own likeness upon the earth; and it was so, even as they ordered.

And the Gods organized the earth to bring forth grass from its own seed, and the herb to bring forth herb from its own seed, yielding seed after his kind; and the earth to bring forth the tree from its own seed, yielding fruit, whose seed could only bring forth the same in itself, after his kind; and the Gods saw that they were obeyed.

And it came to pass that they numbered the days; from the evening until the morning they called night; and it came to pass, from the morning until the evening they called day; and it was the third time."

Abraham 4:11-13

The bringing forth of plant life was a major work of the third creative period. Genesis says the earth "brought forth" (present time) as if the event followed the command immediately. Abraham by contrast says the earth was *organized* to bring forth plant life at some future time. All three accounts mention grass, trees, and herbs, probably to make clear that *all* plant life is to be included. Certainly we can excuse the omission of the seaweeds and microscopic algae of which ancient peoples had no knowledge and for which they had no names.

The puzzle of the creation of plant life is that in all three accounts it comes before the organization of the heavenly bodies including the "greater light that rules the day." How could plant life exist before the sun was in existence? A basic fact of nature is that plants cannot exist in the absence of light. In scientific terms plants cannot live without photosynthesis. What point would there be in producing plants on earth before the basic energy source of the solar system was operating? This is such a hopeless reversal of the common-sense order of things that one would, on the face of it, conclude that the writer of Genesis was inconceivably ignorant or inexcusably careless of the facts. It is such an obvious mistake, one might say, that it appears almost deliberate. Is it a signal thrown up for a purpose? If accepted as an outright error, it alone is sufficient to discourage a scientist from placing much weight on Genesis as a textbook of natural history. If it is not an error, it bears careful looking into.

Consider the language more carefully. For one thing the account in Abraham makes it clear that actual plants were to appear later. No such stipulation is made regarding the sun, moon and stars which were also products of the *third* day.

"And the Gods organized the lights in the expanse of the heaven, and caused them to divide the day from the night; and organized them to be for signs and for seasons, and for days and for years;

And organized them to be for lights in the expanse of the heaven to give light upon the earth; and it was so.

And the Gods organized the two great lights, the greater light to rule the day, and the lesser light to rule the night; with the lesser light they set the stars also;

And the Gods set them in the expanse of the heavens, to give light upon the earth, and to rule over the day and over the night, and to cause to divide the light from the darkness.

And the Gods watched those things which they had
ordered until they obeyed."

Abraham 4:14-18

The conclusion seems justified that the sun and moon were
produced during this third period but plant life was yet to come.
This is in line with a basic message of the creation scriptures:
Inanimate things were organized and finished in the first six periods
while animate things did not appear as "living souls" until the
seventh period.

Other important possibilities are suggested by Genesis 1:11
and equivalent scriptures. In the first place these are the first reference to living things and may have a bearing on the problem of
the origin of life and of its appearance on earth. The distinction
made in the preceding sentence is intended to suggest that the
origin of life is a problem separate and apart from the appearance of
life on earth. Evidence is growing and is accepted by more and more
scientists that life is widespread in the universe and hence did not
originate on the earth at all.

Consider the implications of the discovery and identification of
complex molecules in space as introduced and discussed in connection with water in chapter 11. Investigators have been quick to
realize that many space molecules are essential links between the
simple chemical elements and living matter. Hydrogen cyanide
(HCN) is involved in the proposed pre-life synthesis of animo acids
and purines. Formaldehyde ($H_2C\!:\!O$), the prebiotic (pre-life) precursor of glycine and the sugars, is common. Cyanoacetylene
($HC\!:\!C\text{-}CN$) has been proposed as a precursor of the pyrimidines,
cytosine and uracil. For some unknown reason there seem to be a
strong tendency to form organic (carbon-based) molecules in space.
Students of interstaller matter are convinced that the building up of
organic compounds is going on in a continuous manner and on a
widespread scale.

It is not surprising that the possibility of life arising and existing in interstellar space should be receiving serious attention.
After all, if the essential elements are there together with an almost
complete spectrum of radiant energy, there appears to be no good
reason why life might not arise just as easily in the clouds of space
as in the environment of an earth-like planet. Any living thing small
enough to float freely in the environment of an interstellar cloud
would have a good chance of existing and even of reproducing indefinitely as long as favorable conditions continued. And there is no
reason to suppose that a planet is any more or less permanent or

long enduring than an interstellar cloud. Questions naturally arise as to just what level of complexity might be attained by floating life forms in space. Conditions would appear not to be unfavorable for large molecules, perhaps even cells, provided these could be individually in direct contact with the environment. It is likewise conceivable that such small entities might evolve to the point of being able to obtain energy by photosynthesis—the prerequisites for this basic process ought to be just as prevalent in certain interstellar clouds as they are on certain planets, Earth for example. Recent (1976) studies of the planet Jupiter have added other thoughts on extraterrestrial life. Jupiter has been described as a great "liquid drop" in allusion to the fact that most of it appears to be liquid hydrogen and other liquid components. One near-surface level or shell of the atmosphere consists of water vapor. It is seriously suggested that life could exist in this environment which certainly possesses a number of the basic requirements such as water, a tolerable temperature, and energy sources of several sorts.

One of the most serious problems for photosynthetic organisms is that of maintaining their chloroplasts in the sunlight. They cannot operate in darkness, or under too much water, or in the presence of strong radiation or in too much heat or cold. These are hinderances that earth-bound plant life has adjusted to in various ways. It is possible to conceive situations in interstellar clouds in which many of these difficulties would be much less severe or even non-existent. Space is vast and conditions are varied. It is known that stars evolve from and appear in clouds of water-rich gas and dust. It seems safe to assume that whatever elements are in new stars must also have been in their ancestral clouds. If there are free-floating complex molecules of types that are basic to life, it is only logical to assume that there are also traces of the minor elements that might be essential or at least helpful to the photosynthetic process. Likewise, considering the fact that clouds show varying degrees of opacity to radiation, it is probable that vast belts or zones are present that receive just the proper amount of energy for photosynthesis to operate. What a free-floating existence obviously does not provide is a solid base on which larger structures can grow. Surprisingly, evidence has been found that an earthly bacterium, *Serratia marcescens,* is able to live and reproduce in water vapor in the laboratory.

There are obvious limits to the advancement of life forms in space. Only through the organization of many-celled plants and animals is the ultimate potential of life realized. For these a solid earth-like surface is essential. This is not to deny that there are fish swimming freely in the open ocean and birds in the sky. But these are also under the influence of gravity and couldn't exist without the watery or atmospheric envelops that accompany the earth.

One of the serious theories of how life came to earth is that of Panspermia. This theory assumes that life is widespread in the universe and is carried in spore-like form throughout space. If the proper key molecules or basic living entities fall into an atmosphere favorable for their existence, they may continue to evolve to higher more complex forms of life. Serious papers have been written on the possible "seeding" of the earth by comets. Thus life as we know it need not have originated on earth—it could well have arrived from an unknown place at a time when the earth was ready to receive it. The same "seeding" may have taken place on other planets but there, because of unfavorable conditions, life failed to survive. After all, this is the story of all air-born seeds and spores, a few take root, others do not. Thus it may be more accurate to speak of the *appearance* of life on earth than the *origin* of life on earth. Certainly the idea of Panspermia has much to recommend it especially in view of the discovery of complex molecules in space.

The meaning of this in the context of scriptural interpretation is that the origin of life, specifically, forms which can maintain themselves by radiant energy (plants in the broad sense), need not have been on earth or even in the near vicinity of the earth. All essentials for photosynthetic life forms can be supplied just as well if not better, in interstellar space than they can in a planetary atmosphere or on a solid gravity-dominated surface. In the grand process of creation as hinted at in scriptures and discovered in more detail by modern science the appearance of light is a primary step and light is universal. Light-producing suns come and go as part of an evolutionary process. God informed Moses: "...the heavens, they are many, and they cannot be numbered unto man; but they are numbered unto me, for they are mine. And as one earth shall pass away, and the heavens thereof even so shall another come; and there is no end to my works, neither to my words." (Moses 1:37-38.)

Here may be an explanation for the curious reference to plants in Genesis 2:5: "And every plant of the field before it was in the earth, and every herb of the field before it grew:..." Why are animals and man not included here? All life, not just plants, had a potential or spiritual existence before earth became a suitable habitation. Is this cryptic scripture a reminder that plants (in the broad sense) were actually in existence during the pre-earth period while animals were not?

The seeming illogic of the Genesis story in having plant life appear before the creation of the sun may not be illogical after all. The Genesis order could well be essentially correct, another proof for a divine origin of the scriptures.

Comments and References

The possibility that simple forms of life can originate, evolve, and exist in space is based on the known chemical and physical requirements for life as found on the earth. Any up-to-date encyclopedia article on botany describes the basic requirements of plant cells. A modern college textbook is Raven, Evert and Curtis, 1976, *Biology of Plants,* 2nd edition, Worth Publishers. Less technical and highly illustrated is F. W. Went, 1963, *The Plants,* a volume of the Life Nature Library, Time, Inc. The important interactions between plants and the atmosphere is described in James C. G. Walker, 1977, *Evolution of the Atmosphere,* Macmillan Publishing Co. A book by I. S. Shklovskii and Carl Sagan, 1966, *Intelligent Life in the Universe,* Holden Day, Inc., gives a broader perspective.

Several papers dealing specifically with the possibility of life in interstellar space or on other planets are found in Cyril Ponnamperuma, ed., 1976, *Chemical Evolution of the Giant Planets.* Subjects treated are life at low temperature, life in extreme environments, biological water requirements, and life on Jupiter.

Articles in popular scientific periodicals are: Barry E. Turner, 1973, *Interstellar Molecules:* in Scientific American, March, 1973; R. M. Lemmon, 1976, *Molecules of Life:* in Astronomy, vol. 4, No. 5, and *Jupiter II,* in Science News, July 17, 1976.

21
Two Great Lights...The Stars Also

"And God made two great lights; the greater light to rule the day, and the lesser light to rule the night: he made the stars also."
Genesis 1:16

"And I, God, made two great lights; the greater light to rule the day, and the lesser light to rule the night, and the greater light was the sun, and the lesser light was the moon; and the stars also were made even according to my word."
Moses 2:16

"And the Gods organized the lights in the expanse of the heaven, and caused them to divide the day from the night; and organized them to be for signs and for seasons, and for days and for years;

And organized them to be for lights in the expanse of the heaven to give light upon the earth; and it was so.

And the Gods organized the two great lights, the greater light to rule the day, and the lesser light to rule the night; with the lesser light they set the stars also;

And the Gods set them in the expanse of the heavens, to give light upon the earth, and to rule over the day and over the night, and to cause to divide the light from the darkness."
Abraham 4:14-17

The appearance of the sun and the moon "two great lights" set in the heavens to give light upon the earth is described as an event of the fourth day. That these astronomical bodies should be mentioned as appearing after the earth and even after the creation of plant life on the third day seems to contradict not only common sense but also the basic facts of astronomy. But this is not necessarily so. The emphasis of the scriptures is on the *function* of the sun and the moon as light-givers rather than on their formation as

128

bodies in space. The wording of the scriptures does not prohibit their initial creation on the third day at the same time as the earth. The process by which the sun-earth-moon system came into being has already been briefly described.

Students of scripture have speculated about this problem and had reached logical conclusions a century ago. The key thought in all arguments about the fourth day is that this was the time at which the light of the sun, moon and stars first penetrated to the surface of the earth. I have a small book published by J. H. Ward in 1884 titled *Gospel Philosophy Showing the Absurdities of Infidelity and the Harmony of the Gospel with Science and Religion.* Since the book was published in Salt Lake City Juvenile Instructor Office it may have had a degree of approval by those in charge of Church publications.

In dealing with the events of the third and fourth periods the author of this precocious book remarks: "That the sun and stars had been created long before this (the fourth day), we have no reason to doubt. We may, therefore, correctly infer that they were then for the first time visible from the surface of the earth." (p. 186, italics added)

It is with regard to the nature of the material which prevented the penetration of light to the earth that a modern explanation must differ from that expressed in 1884. Earlier thinkers invisioned a shroud of watery clouds in the earth's atmosphere; today the obstructing material would be classified as dust and gas spread throughout the solar system. Any and all successful theories of the origin of the solar system start with a cloud of matter from which the sun, planets, satellites, comets and meteorites emerged. The gradual clumping together or gathering of material to make these separate solid bodies constitutes what is generally called the origin of the solar system or solar family. A late stage in the process was the clearing away of left-over remnants of dust and gas so that light could penetrate freely throughout the system. This relatively late stage of organization is entirely appropriate to the fourth period of the Genesis account.

Another topic deserves mention here. It is discussed as an explanation for those who might be inclined to retain the more literal view that the sun, moon and stars did not merely *appear* on the fourth day but that they actually did come into existence on that day.

Although Genesis describes the works of creation in a definite six-part sequence it is also clear that there could have been considerable overlap in the events that are described. As any storyteller knows there are difficulties in describing a series of simultaneous ongoing events taking place at separate localities. Of necessity the story follows a particular chain of events at one place to a certain point and then goes back to do the same for events at a second locality. In the terminology of the movies there are "flashbacks" or other devices to show relationships of overlapping or simultaneous events. The human mind can concentrate on only one subject at a time and the reader, or viewer even in imagination, can be in only one place at a time.

Thus Genesis describes mainly a series of separate consecutive events but there are also overlapping situations. Are we, for example, to suppose that the creation of the entire plant world was over and done with before the creation of any animals whatever? As plants and animals exist today they are essential to each other— plants provide food and oxygen for the consumption of animals while animals provide carbon dioxide for the photosynthesis of plants. Bees need flowers, flowers need bees. This is not to deny that in the history of the earth plants preceded animals and in their simple beginnings existed without benefit of animal life. Only later did their histories become interdependent and parallel.

A similar situation probably prevails in reference to the inanimate world of astronomical bodies. The record says: "And God made two great lights; the greater light to rule the day, and the lesser light to rule the night: he made the stars also." Genesis 1:16. If the order in which they are mentioned is to be strictly followed, we must presume that the creation of the sun came first, then the moon, and finally the stars. Astronomers would scoff at the idea that the sun and the moon were produced before any of the stars. Common sense as well as the best scientific theory tells us that the phrase "he made the stars also" is not to be understood as placing the creation of stars in any particular rigid position in the order of creation. After all there is good evidence that stars are forming at the present time. The statement about the stars was surely inserted to complete the record and what better place to include it than in a verse dealing with other astronomical matters? This guarantees that men should be informed that God did indeed create all things in heaven and earth.

We are frequently told that the ancients were great astronomers. While not disputing this it seems safe to say that little of a reliable or profound nature came down to today's scientists. What we know or think we know about astronomical matters has been won in historical time by slow degrees and by the labors of numerous identifiable individuals. It would seem that God left it up to man to discover by his own intellect how the stars were made. But let it be said that astronomers are the first to admit the incompleteness of their knowledge; much remains to be learned.

Latter-day scriptures by comparison with Genesis have a great deal to say about astronomical matters. The Book of Abraham makes several pertinent statements particularly in the explanation of Facsimile Number 2. Some important points are: Kolob is one of the great governing bodies of the system to which we belong. It is "The first creation nearest to the celestial, or the residence of God. First in government, the last pertaining to the measurement of time. The measurement according to celestial time, which celestial time signifies one day to a cubit. One day in Kolob is equal to a thousand years, according to the measurements of this earth.... The celestial body which stands next to Kolob is called by the Egyptians Oliblish...which is the next grand governing creation near the celestial or the place where God resides; holding the key of power also, pertaining to other planets...." We are told further that one thousand answers "to the measuring of the time of Oliblish, which is equal with Kolob in its revolution and in the measuring of time." Another body is identified as being "...one of the governing planets also, and is said by the Egyptians to be the Sun, and to borrow its light from Kolob through the medium of Kae-e-vanrash, which is the grand Key, or, in other words, the governing power, which governs fifteen other fixed planets or stars as also Floeese or the Moon, the earth and the sun in their annual revolutions. This planet receives its power through the medium of Kli-flos-is-es or Hah-ko-kau-beam, the stars represented by numbers 22 and 23, receiving light from the revolution of Kolob." Latter-day Saints have placed various interpretations on the astronomical notations in the Book of Abraham. Some have found in them evidence that Abraham was far ahead of his time and even that his astronomy is fundamentally better than that of today's contemporary scientists. Others believe that Abraham's understanding was that of the Egyptians. Still another view is that neither Abraham nor inspiration have anything to do with the matter, the views expressed being those of Joseph Smith who concocted the whole thing from his meager knowledge and mystical imaginings.

Strange as it seems there may be elements of truth in all these views. Accepting for the moment the thought that these scriptures, like the creation account of Genesis, are deliberately vague, incomplete, and cryptic but still basically true I take the position that they contain enough advanced information to prove that their source was the Creator himself. The task of full interpretation obviously lies in the future.

Comments and References

The text of this chapter deals with the stars, the sun, and the moon, a subject matter so vast that an overwhelming amount of literature has been produced by those who are specialists in astronomy, astrogeology, cosmology and cosmogony. References are available at all levels of technicality. Those listed in connection with previous chapters should be consulted. Popular textbooks which treat the origin of stars are Stanley Wyatt, *Principles of Astronomy,* 2nd Ed., 1971, Allyn and Bacon; Robert H. Baker and Laurence W. Fredrick, 1971, *Astronomy,* Von Nostrand Reinhold Co.; Thornton Page and L. W. Page (eds.), 1968, *The Evolution of Stars,* Macmillin; Lyman Spitzer and A. C. W. Cameron (eds.), 1966, *Stellar Evolution,* Plenum Press; Jay M. Pasachoff, 1977, *Contemporary Astronomy,* Saunders. A good book on the solar system is William K. Hartmann, 1972, *Moons and Planets,* Bogden and Quigley; for data on the planets see Nicholas M. Short, 1975, *Planetary Geology,* Prentice-Hall; a popular book on the sun is George Gamow, 1964, *A Star Called the Sun,* Viking.

Encyclopedia articles on numberous astronomical topics are accessible in libraries. The popular magazine *Astronomy* is widely distributed, and astronomical events and discoveries appear in the news almost daily.

22

Let the Waters Bring Forth... The Moving Creature...Fifth Day

"And God said, Let the waters bring forth abundantly the moving creature that hath life, and fowl that may fly above the earth in the open firmament of heaven."

Genesis 1:20

"And I, God, said: Let the waters bring forth abundantly the moving creature that hath life, and fowl which may fly above the earth in the open firmament of heaven."

Moses 2:20

"And the Gods said: Let us prepare the waters to bring forth abundantly the moving creatures that have life; and the fowl, that they may fly above the earth in the open expanse of heaven.

And the Gods prepared the waters that they might bring forth great whales, and every living creature that moveth, which the waters were to bring forth abundantly after their kind; and every winged fowl after their kind. And the Gods saw that they would be obeyed, and that their plan was good.

And the Gods said: We will bless them, and cause them to be fruitful and multiply, and fill the waters in the seas or great waters; and cause the fowl to multiply in the earth.

And it came to pass that it was from evening until morning that they called night; and it came to pass that it was from morning until evening that they called day; and it was the fifth time."

Abraham 4:20-23

The above texts pertain to the appearance of animal life in the waters of the earth. The event is in its logical place in a sequence—first came plant life which may have appeared in interstellar space; second, animal life appeared in the waters of the earth on this, the fifth day, and later on the sixth day came land life. In distinguishing

133

plants from animals the scriptures make use of the same basic characteristic by which science distinguishes them. Plants are immobile, animals are mobile. *A moving creature that hath life* is an excellent description of an animal as distinguished from a plant. (Readers with more technical knowledge will pardon lack of reference to plants that move such as slime molds, or animals that are fixed in place such as oysters.) Scriptural matters are of more immediate concern at this point.

All three scriptural sources tell the same story but with significantly different emphasis. Most important similarity is the assertion that the elements of earth and water have a distinct role in the bringing forth of life. Most important difference has to do with the time when the products of creation were to come forth. The word "let" employed in Genesis and Moses has a number of meanings. In addition to introducing a command it might also request an opportunity or make a plea. Any of these three might be intended by the simple sentence: Let me go. Is the wording of Genesis intended to designate a commandment, an invitation, or an admonition? The wording of Abraham is much more instructive and specific than either Genesis or Moses. Here the Gods are represented as preparing and organizing earth and water to produce life at some future time. From Genesis and Moses a reader would almost surely be led to believe that the appearance of the different life forms was immediate with no delay and no lengthy preparations necessary. Abraham suggests evolution, Genesis favors creationism.

The origin of life has always been a topic of great interest to man no matter what his stage of development and civilization has been. Primitive explanations exist in numerous myths and legends. These almost always contain magical and supernatural elements and are of obvious human origin. The idea of spontaneous generation by natural means is basic to any discussion of the origin of life. Many common observations justify a belief that higher animals can come from lower ones—thus caterpillars do become butterflies and tadpoles do become frogs. And it was not too difficult to believe that inanimate matter gives rise to complex living things. Flies are seen to crawl from dung heaps and mice scurry out of piles of old rags without obvious outside parentage. The belief that living things might thus originate from dead matter or lower beings was held by the learned as well as the common man during ancient and medieval times. Support for the theory of spontaneous generation also comes naturally from a literal reading of the Scriptures. After all the Bible plainly asserts that earth and water have the power to bring forth plants and animals as long as God permits it.

Spontaneous generation as it was understood in medieval times was discredited by the famous experiments of Louis Pasteur. His well-known demonstration was to expose one specimen of broth to ready access of air-borne spores and an identical specimen to air but not to spores. As he confidently predicted, the first specimen was contaminated the second was not. Other experimenters went on to show that fly eggs are always necessary for the production of flies and that litters of young mice must always come from pregnant mother mice. Now no one believes that higher forms of life come spontaneously from non-living matter.

Although Pasteur's experiments were hailed as a triumph for the experimental method they brought also a rather embarrassing and unexpected threat to science. If life cannot come by spontaneous generation, how did it come in the first place? Obviously there is only one alternative—special creation. Since scientists are generally unwilling to accept a supernatural alternative they have had to admit the possibility that life has arisen, at least once, by spontaneous generation. The opinions of many if not most of those who are working in the field of biogenesis, which has to do with the origin of life, is that life could have arisen in a spontaneous manner *when conditions were right.*

That conditions must have been right at least once cannot be denied by either an atheistic scientist or a fundamentalist theologian. The scientist believes that life came by a spontaneous process and has been able to exist and progress on available resources over billions of years of time. The theologian believes that God acted upon the available materials of the earth which were ample and sufficient to support life thereafter for an apparently infinite period. God may have made earth out of nothing but living things were made of dust. And God considered his creations to be good and so pronounced them.

The inescapable conclusion is that *it is the organization of the elements and not their original production that is important.* This same basic truth was evident in previous steps of creation, particularly in regard to the earth as a planet. And what does organization mean? It means to arrange, to form, or to assemble simpler things into more complex things. Organization is God's method of creation. Joseph Smith described it well:

"You ask the learned doctors why they say the world was made out of nothing; and they will answer, 'Doesn't the Bible say He *created* the world?' And they infer, from the word create, that it must have been made out of nothing.

Now, the word create came from the word *baurau* which does not mean to create out of nothing; it means to organize; the same as a man would organize materials and build a ship. Hence, we infer that God had materials to organize the world out of chaos—chaotic matter, which is element, and in which dwells all the glory. Element had an existence from the time he had. The pure principles of element are principles which can never be destroyed; they may be organized and re-organized, but not destroyed. They had no beginning, and can have no end." (Teachings of the Prophet Joseph Smith, p. 350.)

How but by inspiration and revelation could Joseph Smith in 1844 state so clearly, confidently and correctly the principle of conservation of matter-energy that science was not to understand until more than a century later?

The language of Abraham, allows no other conclusion but that the organization of the elements was made in anticipation of future fulfillment. In other words, the coming forth of living things did not follow immediately the gathering together, preparation or organization of the elements. Conditions were not yet propitious for organic beings. They could only become possible with the watering of the earth at the beginning of the seventh day.

Leaving aside the actual appearance of life, which for purposes of argument may be regarded as an entirely natural, indeed, inevitable product of the right organization of things we can profitably consider what it is that must precede the event itself. Scientifically speaking, Earth became qualified as an abode of life not by a last minute accident or miraculous reorganization of a barren planet but through a lengthy series of events which we are only now beginning to understand. Since the earth is our best and only known example of a habitable planet, its pre-life history is of paramount importance in any theory of creation. A brief tabulation of the prerequisites for life as we know it is appropriate:

1. Essential Elements: All earth life requires certain chemical elements. These enter into the composition of all protoplasm no matter whether it makes up the simplest bacterium or a human brain. Hydrogen, carbon, nitrogen, oxygen, phosphorus and sulphur make up at least 95 per cent of all protoplasm, and other prominent constituents are potassium, sodium, magnesium, calcium, and chlorine. Most organisms also require traces of iron, copper, zinc, manganese, molybdenum, boron, fuorine, silicon, iodine and other elements.

All these elements must be and in fact are widely distributed everywhere on earth so as to be available to living things in all environments. It is not enough that the essential elements be present on the surface of the planet; all those mentioned are present on the Moon and probably on Mars but they are fixed in unbreakable combinations or are otherwise unavailable to life.

2. Water: Protoplasm is 80 per cent water. Hydrogen and oxygen, the components of water, may be present in rocks and minerals but there must be a great excess of these elements for the production of the vast quantities of water such as exist on earth. Water is the great universal solvent and the agent which transports and distributes the other essential elements throughout the earth. This it accomplishes in running streams, in slowly percolating films in the soil, and in great currents that stir the entire ocean.

A little thought will convince anyone that other means of accomplishing the essential fluxing of elements exist on the planet Earth. Glaciers remove, grind up, mix, and redeposit sediment. Volcanic eruptions spew out pulverized dust from diverse subterranian sources to create temporarily lifeless but potentially fertile beds of ash. The wind picks up and carries dust particles everywhere; when these settle, they constitute the most fertile soils on earth. Large sectors of Europe, China, and North America were blanketed by wind-blown soil (loess) during the Ice Age and now support a large fraction of mankind.

The slow-moving currents of the so-called "solid" earth accomplish the greatest mixing of all. Material from the ocean basins slowly moves toward great downsinking belts where it is melted and assimulated. Much of the melted material rises to the surface again to become part of the continents. What was formerly thought to be lost forever to the oceans is now known to return, even though very slowly, to build up the land.

3. Correct Temperature: Evidences of water action throughout most of the geologic rock record is direct proof that the temperature has remained tolerable for immense periods of time. The temperature span between the freezing and boiling points of water (0-100°) is almost by definition the range in which life can exist. Protoplasm must die if these limits are exceeded for any great length of time. Considering the great range of temperatures that exist in the universe it must be counted as providential, fortunate, or extremely unusual that the surface of the earth has remained within a very narrow temperature range. Not only was the temperature favorable for life to originate, it has also remained within tolerable even comfortable limits ever since.

These brief comments suggest basic ways in which water takes part in life-supporting processes. Other roles of water in pre-life creative events have been mentioned in chapters 11 and 20. The wording used in the opening quotations of this chapter might be interpreted in two ways. Either water itself might be produced or previously existing water might be provided with the proper environment in which it could fulfill its intended role. The last interpretation seems preferable. Water may exist in clouds of space, in the depths of the earth or in ice or stream or vapor on the surface but it would not be suitable in these forms for supporting advanced animal life. The final preparation of water, mentioned as an event of the fifth day, comes when the earth itself is so organized and situated with regard to the central sun that water can exist and circulate in liquid and gaseous form.

The hydrological cycle is one of the marvels of the earth's physical systems. For it to operate there must be a large liquid reservoir in the form of oceans and seas from which water vapor may escape by evaporation. The atmospheric moisture must then be carried by air currents to localities where it is forced to condense and fall as snow or rain. On the earth it gathers by gravity into streams that flow downward to the general ocean. On its journey through the ocean and sky and across the land water comes in contact with all forms of life. Were it not for the environment provided by the earth, water could not carry out its essential role in supporting life as it is known on earth.

Comments and References

The topic of this chapter is the appearance of animal life on earth and in its waters. Much has been written on the subject and the trend in this writing has been steadily away from the idea of supernatural, instantaneous origin and toward natural, gradual, and long term processes devoid of supernatural manifestations. An excellent discussion of various explanations of the origin of life is Charles H. Long, 1963, *Alpha, the Myths of Creation,* George Brasiller. Some general references written in the scientific vein are H. F. Blum, 1968, *Times Arrow and Evolution,* 3rd ed., Princeton University Press; H. Calvin, 1969, *Chemical Evolution,* Oxford University Press; Stanley L. and L. E. Orgel, 1974, *The Origins of Life on Earth,* Prentice-Hall, Inc.; M. G. Rulten, 1971, *The Origin of Life by Natural Causes,* Elsevier; S. W. Fox (ed.), 1965, *The Origin of Pre-biological Systems,* Academic Press.

A seimi-popular easily understandable book that is entirely evolutionary in approach is Ruth Moore and the Editors of Life, 1964, *Evolution,* Time, Inc. The entire September 1978 issue of Scientific American is devoted to the single topic of organic evolution. For anyone having only limited time this is perhaps the most factual and comprehensive reference available.

Anti-evolution literature may be obtained from the Institute for Creation Research (ICR), 2716 Madison Avenue, San Diego, California 92116. Titles available from this source include: *Scientific Creationism; Evolution? The Fossils Say No!; The Genesis Record; Bible Cosmology and Modern Science; The Bible and Modern Science,* and many others. Over a period of many years the *Plain Truth* magazine issued by the Worldwide Church of God has carried many anti-evolution articles.

23

Beast of the Earth...Cattle... Creeping Thing...Man...Sixth Day

"And God said, Let the earth bring forth the living creature after his kind, cattle, and creeping thing, and beast of the earth after his kind: and it was so.

And God made the beast of the earth after his kind, and cattle after their kind, and every thing that creepeth upon the earth after his kind; and God saw that it was good.

And God said, Let us make man in our image, after our likeness: and let them have dominion over the fish of the sea, and over the fowl of the air, and over the cattle, and over all the earth, and over every creeping thing that creepeth upon the earth.

So God created man in his own image, in the image of God created he him; male and female created he them.

And God blessed them, and God said unto them, Be fruitful, and multiply, and replenish the earth, and subdue it: and have dominion over the fish of the sea, and over the fowl of the air, and over every living thing that moveth upon the earth.

And God said, Behold, I have given you every herb bearing seed, which is upon the face of all the earth, and every tree, in the which is the fruit of a tree yielding seed; to you it shall be for meat.

And to every beast of the earth, and to every fowl of the air, and to every thing that creepeth upon the earth, wherein there is life, I have given every green herb for meat: and it was so.

And God, saw every thing that he had made, and, behold, it was very good. And the evening and the morning were the sixth day."

Genesis 1:24-31

"And I, God, said: Let the earth bring forth the living creature after his kind, cattle, and creeping things, and beasts of the earth after their kind, and it was so;

And I, God, made the beasts of the earth after their kind, and cattle after their kind, and everything which creepeth upon the earth after his kind; and I, God, saw that these things were good.

140

And I, God, said unto mine Only Begotten, which was with me from the beginning: Let us make man in our image, after our likeness; and it was so. And I, God, said: Let them have dominion over the fishes of the sea, and over the fowl of the air, and over the cattle, and over all the earth, and over every creeping thing that creepeth upon the earth.

And I, God, created man in mine own image, in the image of mine Only Begotten created I him; male and female created I them.

And I, God, blessed them, and said unto them: Be fruitful, and multiply, and replenish the earth, and subdue it, and have dominion over the fish of the sea, and over the fowl of the air, and over every living thing that moveth upon the earth.

And I, God, said unto man: Behold, I have given you every herb bearing seed, which is upon the face of all the earth, and every tree in the which shall be the fruit of a tree yielding seed; to you it shall be for meat.

And to every beast of the earth, and to every fowl of the air, and to everything that creepeth upon the earth, wherein I grant life, there shall be given every clean herb for meat; and it was so, even as I spake.

And I, God, saw everything that I had made, and, behold, all things which I had made were very good; and the evening and the morning were the sixth day.''

Moses 2:24-31

"And the Gods prepared the earth to bring forth the living creature after his kind, cattle and creeping things, and beasts of the earth after their kind; and it was so, as they had said.

And the Gods organized the earth to bring forth the beasts after their kind, and cattle after their kind, and every thing that creepeth upon the earth after its kind; and the Gods saw they would obey.

And the Gods took counsel among themselves and said: Let us go down and form man in our image after our likeness; and we will give them dominion over the fish of the sea, and over the fowl of the air, and over the cattle, and over all the earth, and over every creeping thing that creepeth upon the earth.

So the Gods went down to organize man in their own image, in the image of the Gods to form they him, male and female to form they them.

And the Gods said: We will bless them. And the Gods said: We will cause them to be fruitful and multiply, and replenish the earth, and subdue it, and to have dominion over the fish of the sea, and over the fowl of the air, and over every living thing that moveth upon the earth.

And the Gods said: Behold, we will give them every herb bearing seed that shall come upon the face of all the earth, and every tree which shall have fruit upon it; yea, the fruit of the tree yielding seed to them we will give it; it shall be for their meat.

And to every beast of the earth, and to every fowl of the air, and to every thing that creepeth upon the earth, behold, we will give them life, and also we will give to them every green herb for meat, and all these things shall be thus organized.

And the Gods said: We will do everything that we have said, and organize them; and behold, they shall be very obedient. And it came to pass that it was from evening until morning they called night; and it came to pass that it was from morning until evening that they called day; and they numbered the sixth time.''

Abraham 4:24-31

A great deal of information is contained in the eight verses that describe the events of the sixth day. This is understandable as it was during this period that higher forms of animal life and man himself appeared. The first two verses pertain to all land-living animals: "creeping things" no doubt designates most insects, the less common crawling or walking invertebrates such as snails and even many reptiles and amphibians. "Cattle" and "beasts of the field" would seem to comprise both wild and domestic mammals. The Bible follows the same sequence as geology and biology textbooks which recognize an age of sea life followed by an age of land life. According to the findings of those who study ancient life the age of animal land life began with the emergence of air-breathing invertebrates and vertebrates in the Devonian Period about 400 million years ago. By then plants were already established on land but had not been there for long. It is one of the mysteries of the history of life that colonization of the lands was so long delayed. A believable explanation is that exposure to the full power of sunlight is dangerous and deadly and would have been fatal until atmospheric oxygen had accumulated in sufficient quantity to constitute the ozone layer that now forms a protective shield around the globe. It seems ironical that earth's highest creature, man, now has the power to destroy the ozone layer and in fact may be doing so.

Three verses of the sixth-day description are devoted to the subject of man, stressing the points that he was created in the image of the Gods, that both male and female appeared, that mankind should be fruitful in multiplying and replenishing himself, that he should subdue the earth and, finally that he sould have dominion over all other living things. The instruction to multiply, and replenish, to take dominion over other species and to subdue the earth seems to have been followed by mankind to an ultimate extreme, even to a fault as it were. The twin problems of overpopulation and depletion of resources are now mankind's chief concern. Has man become too fruitful? Has he subdued the earth too thoroughly, perhaps to the point of harming it in incurable ways? These are problems that go far beyond the scope of this book and in spite of their importance cannot be considered further here.

Two verses out of six are devoted to what are plainly dietary matters. Basic is the assertion that all animal land life (including fowls) are to seek and find their food supply in the vegetable world. This appears to be self evident today. Significantly the word green is used in describing plants that are intended for food. Science might translate this into a reference to photosynthesis which is the basic food (energy) producing process for all life, both plant and animal. Since the directive is clear that the "meat" of man should be from herbs and trees one might ponder the thought that by well-managed vegetarianism the food shortages and dietary ills of the world might be alleviated.

It is easy to forget in reading Genesis and Moses that the creations of the sixth day, namely animal land life and man are not to appear as actual beings until the seventh day. It was the physical preparations that took place on the sixth day. Since the preparations for sea life had been completed on the fifth day there must have been something significantly different having to do with land life that was not yet accomplished on the pre-life earth during the fifth day. And if our analysis is right, both preparations for sea life and the preparations for land life took place before it rained on the earth. How can these constraints be satisfied?

A possible sequence of events is strongly suggested by recent scientific discoveries but the details will undoubtedly need refinement. According to the best current theory the waters of the earth came out of the interior as it cooled from a molten condition or solidified to a compact state. The capacity to produce water must be counted as the most obviously essential attribute of a planet intended to support seas and oceans. Yet, the capacity to produce water or even its actual production is not necessarily equivalent to the filling of the oceans or even the production of rain. What is found on Mars supports this statement. Mars has water but there are neither oceans nor life as far as we can tell.

There was probably a stage in the history of the planet when all liquid or gaseous materials including water that reached the surface were swept away as soon as they appeared. An entirely effective mechanism for doing this exists in the radiation pressure from the sun (solar wind) that was probably much stronger at that early time. In other words the earth had already "come up dry" and was capable of producing water but the accumulation of water bodies on its surface was for a time prevented by external forces.

What is there in the above situation that is unfavorable to the ultimate appearance of land life? An answer is obvious, there are no provisions for land or more specifically for continents. One can easily imagine a globe entirely flooded by water. On the face of it this should be the structure of the earth—first, a sphere of solid material, then a layer of water, and finally an atmosphere, all these being in successive layers according to density. As far as we know the interior of the earth is a succession of shells neatly constructed of nested spheres surrounding a heavy central core. The gaseous envelope is likewise composed of a half-dozen world-circling "spheres" ranging from heavier to lighter outward. Only the water or hydro-sphere breaks the neat expectable pattern. The water of the earth is not in a continuous layer even though it might well be. There is enough water to form an unbroken world-circling ocean 8,000 feet deep. But it is the continents that break up the continuity of the water not the water that breaks up the continuity of the land.

Why continents? Why is the lighter material of the earth's crust piled up in irregular pancake-like patches rather than being in a uniform layer as might be expected? The problem looms even larger when it is realized that erosion by water, wind and ice is continually at work to wear down the land. The fact is that continents have been in existence for a very long time, several billion years according to geologic reckoning, and yet they seem to be just as large and high as they ever were.

In spite of their present prominence and apparent durability there must have been a time when there were no continents, and even more important, no mechanism for creating and maintaining them. When the earth was molten and for a while thereafter the surface material of the globe was probably quite uniformly distributed. There were no elevated land masses that could become continents or basins to contain oceans when water became available.

How continents were made and are maintained has now been explained by a very satisfactory theory. The process goes by the name of sea-floor spreading. Space again prohibits a complete discussion but there are many good non-technical explanations. Briefly the process is this: From a great system of world-circling submarine mountains that more or less bisect the great ocean basins lava is emerging from within the earth on a grand scale. This material does not pile up, it rises and fills an ever-widening rift or great crack as the sides move apart. It is not understood why this rift system continues to open but it clearly has been doing so for an immense period of time. Earthquakes and volcanoes accompany the general unrest. The most amazing fact about the process is that the material thus created is carried away or pushed aside to become part of the ocean bottom. In time any strip of once-liquid lava is displaced tens, hundreds and even thousands of miles away from its original position. This is what is called sea-floor spreading. The ocean basins are splitting apart.

But it is obvious that the sea bottoms cannot expand indefinitely without encountering a continent or another section of ocean bottom. It doesn't help to know that some continents are carried or pushed along by the expanding process, even these must eventually collide with other sections—the space on the earth's surface is constant. The great moving plates, some with continents, some without, do inevitably collide and it is what happens along the colliding fronts that neatly explains how the process works and what causes continents. When two plates push together, one usually is forced downward and is overridden by the other. South America, for example, is pushing over the Pacific plate, the ascending plate is being forceably elevated into the Andes chain. The descending plate does not remain intact and inert—almost at once it begins to melt and soon is consumed into the heated plastic layer below. The material of which a descending plate is composed thus becomes part of the world-circling reservoir below and can be extruded again at the mid-ocean ridges to complete the cycle.

Very important to note is that when ocean meets continent, it is the oceanic plates that are forced downward; they are heavier and lower to begin with. However, a great deal of lighter material from these plates is literally scraped off against the continents to make them wider and even higher. Also, once a plate melts its lighter constituents tend to rise and break forth in volcanoes adding still more material to the lands. This is the origin of the volcanic ring-of-fire around the Pacific Ocean. That these volcanoes are busily making new islands and adding to older lands is a matter of observation.

The whole concept of splitting volcanic mountains, spreading sea floors, colliding continents and recycling of earth materials generally is conveyed by the term plate tectonics, or global tectonics. It is a view of things that has revolutionized earth science on a par with the Copernican revolution in astronomy and the Darwinian revolution in biology. Its importance to our present subject is that the beginning of the land (continent) building process must have happened in the distant past after the cooling of the interior of the earth but before the appearance of fossils. Geologists are agreed that the process of plate tectonics is a phenomenon that would be expected in a cooling layered planet such as earth. That no other planet of the solar system has been thus affected or has the proper structure and internal composition to be affected is now evident. Earth becomes more unusual with each space mission.

In the context of scriptural interpretations the preparation of earth (land) to bring forth or support air-breathing animal life was the work of the sixth creative period. Mechanisms had to be set up that would permit land life to emerge when conditions were right. Such a land-creating and land-maintaining mechanism is now evident and it became operative at the right time in the scriptural creation sequence.

Comments and References

One of the last stages in the preparation of the earth was the appearance of land areas suitable for the air-breathing animals that were destined to appear. The process by which continents and islands are created has been discovered and is known by the scientific name of plate tectonics. The subject has received wide publicity and since about 1970 has been integrated into textbooks at all levels. The following general geology books are recommended: W. L. Stokes, Sheldon Judson, and M. D. Picard, 1978, *Introduction to Geology*, Prentice-Hall; L. Don Leet, Sheldon Judson, and M. E. Kauffman, 1978, *Physical Geology*, Prentice-Hall; Frank Press and Raymond Siever, 1974, *Earth*, Freeman.

Books dealing specifically with the subject of the development of the earth's major features as explained by plate tectonics are: A. A. Hallam, 1971, *A Revolution in Earth Sciences: From Continental Drift to Plate Tectonics*, Oxford University Press; Ursula B. Marvin, 1973, *Continental Drift: The Evolution of a Concept*, Smithsonian Institution Press; Walter Sullivan, 1974, *Continents in Motion: The New Earth Debate*, McGraw-Hill. A collection of excellent papers from the Scientific American is J. Tuzo Wilson (ed.), 1972,

Continents Adrift, Freeman. A follow-up selection from the same source is *Continents Adrift and Continents Aground,* 1976.

The National Geographic Magazine has published two excellent articles: Samuel W. Matthews, This Changing Earth, January 1973; and J. R. Steirtzler and Emery Kristof, Project Famous, May, 1975. Articles in other popular magazines are: Tom Alexander, A revolution called plate tectonics has given us a whole new earth, *Smithsonian,* January 1975; Dan R. McKenzie, Plate tectonics and seafloor spreading, *American Scientist,* July-August, 1972.

24

After His Kind

"And God said, Let the earth bring forth grass, and herb yielding seed, and the fruit tree yielding fruit after his kind....

And the earth brought forth grass...herb...tree...after his kind and God saw that it was good.

And God created great whales, and every living creature that moveth, which the waters brought forth abundantly, after their kind, and every winged fowl after his kind....

And God said let the earth bring forth the living creature after his kind, cattle and creeping thing, and beast of the earth after his kind...

And God made the beast of the earth after his kind, and cattle after their kind, and every thing that creepeth upon the earth after his kind...."

Genesis 1:11-25

"And the earth brought forth grass, every herb yielding seed after his kind, and the tree yielding fruit...after his kind.

And I, God, created great whales, and every living creature... after their kind...every winged fowl after his kind...

And I, God, made the beasts of the earth after their kind... cattle...everything that creepeth upon the earth...after his kind."

Moses 2:11-25

"And the Gods said: Let us prepare the earth to bring forth grass; the herb yielding seed; the fruit tree yielding fruit, after his kind...

And the Gods organized the earth to bring forth grass...herb... tree...after his kind.

And the Gods prepared the waters to bring forth...great whales...every living creature...every winged fowl after their kind.

And the Gods organized the earth to bring forth the beasts after their kind, and cattle after their kind, and every thing that creepeth upon the earth after its kind...

Abraham 4:11-25

148

So far as the creation of plants and animals is concerned these are critical scriptures. Some of the important concepts they contain have already been discussed. What is to be emphasized here are those scattered passages that illustrate usages of the phrase *after his kind* or *after their kind.*

It is often said that the scriptures explain themselves. A problem raised by one verse may often be explained by a verse somewhere else. This is the reason men search, and do not merely read the scriptures. Certain it is that only by cross-reference and comparison can a student be sure that he has at least looked at all the evidence. There are thirty occurrences of the phrase "after his kind" in the Bible. Nine of these are in the first chapter of Genesis, seven are in Genesis 6-7, one is in Genesis 8, nine are in Leviticus 11, and four are in Deuteronomy 14. Here then is an unusual abundance of comparative usages.

As the phrase in question appears in Genesis 6, 7 and 8 it has to do with the Flood and Noah's Ark in particular. Noah was instructed as follows:

> "And of every living thing of all flesh, two of every sort shalt thou bring into the ark, to keep them alive with thee; they shall be male and female.
> Of fowls after their kind, and of cattle after their kind, of every creeping thing of the earth after his kind, two of every sort shall come unto thee, to keep them alive."
>
> Genesis 6:19-20

The animals that entered the ark when the rain came are described:

> "...and every beast after his kind, and all the cattle after their kind, and every creeping thing...after his kind... every fowl after his kind, every bird of every sort.
> And they went in unto Noah into the ark two and two of all flesh...."
>
> Genesis 7:14-15

At a later date in Hebrew history it again became necessary to deal with large groupings of animals in relation to their use as food. In Leviticus 11 instructions are given as to "what may be eaten and what may not, of beast, of fishes and of fowls." The following verses are pertinent here:

"And the vulture and the kite after his kind;
Every raven after his kind;
And the owl, and the night hawk, and the cuckow, and
the hawk after his kind,
And the stork, the heron after her kind, and the lap-
wing, and the bat.
Even these of them ye may eat; the locust after his
kind, and the beetle after his kind, and the grasshopper
after his kind."

What do these usages of "after his kind" have in common? In the creation episode the phrase occur in connection with the bring-ing forth of living things especially as these are mentioned in certain natural groupings such as grass, herbs, trees, moving crea-tures, winged fowl, cattle, etc. In the flood story the usage is in con-nection with the creatures Noah was to bring into the Ark, again in certain groupings such as fowl, cattle, beasts of the field, and creeping things. Finally in the dietary instructions of Leviticus the term "after his kind" again designates certain related species that are not to be eaten. It is not to be wondered at that since there are more birds than there are mammals greater detail as to what is to be eaten had to be given. Although the Leviticus listing becomes quite specific it still does not name all the species—what is named are genera or families instead.

All scriptural uses of "after his kind" appear when there is a necessity to classify, enumerate, or designate by groups a large number of species. This is reasonable. When the need to name a great number of related things involves dozens, hundreds or thou-sands of names one must consolidate and abbreviate. There are many devices such as using et cetra, the familiar etc. In a textbook giving the basic classification of plants and animals I find it con-venient to name one or two common examples and the rest by in-ference under the term "kin"; thus, oysters and kin, starfish and kin, mushrooms and kin. Obviously this device is a great time and space saver in writing and thinking. On the other hand it leaves much to the imagination and much room for uncertainty and dispute. A precise and complete classification or enumeration would require a lengthy list with everything in its place. The reminder that about 2 million living things have already been named indicates the scope of the problem.

The whole subject of what is intended by use of the word "kind" in the creation scripture might be dropped at this point with the conclusion that it is merely a convenient phrase like etc., "and kin," or "such like." Perfectly good sense can be made of phraseology such as "cattle and such like," "beasts of the earth and such like," and "the owl...and his kin," or "the raven and such like."

To drop the subject here, however, leaves too many things unanswered. Even though the intent of scripture was to present an inclusive classification in shortened form this has evidently not been the message received by most readers. The idea that "after his kind" has to do with reproduction seems to dominate most interpretations of Genesis 1 and 2. "After his kind" is commonly taken to mean that each originally created plant or animal "kind" must reproduce unchanged and unchanging until the end of its existence. That which was created as an amoeba can never be anything but an amoeba, a worm nothing but a worm, a monkey nothing but a monkey. This concept has received the designation of the "fixity of species" and is a cornerstone of anti-evolutionary or Creationist belief. Obviously the idea that one kind of organism is prohibited by divine decree from giving rise to another kind needs to be examined in connection with the subject matter of this chapter.

What is a Kind?

One of the marks of a good language is that it contains words that are specific and words that are general. Thus English provides the word *species* that is specific and the word *kind* that is general. It is fortunate that the word kind has not been given a specific meaning and is still open to use in the common vernacular. Furthermore, kind has served a general function ever since it was used in early biblical translations. The first use of the word species in a technical sense was in the mid 16th century but other categories of the present system of biological nomenclature were not used formally until later. In the mid-18th century the "great namer," Carl von Linne (Linnaeus) brought out a system with six levels: kingdom, class, order, genus, species, and variety. This means that in the earlier translations of the Bible the word kind could have had only a very general meaning and only subsequently could it possibly be equated with anything scientific at all.

Everyone knows that there are many distinct kinds of living things. A scientist might substitute the word species for kinds in the above sentence but if he does, he is using a technical term and should be expected to define it. At first this seems easy enough— things that look alike are the same species. But it is not this simple. Several hundred years of study and observation have seemingly made the problem of defining a species more difficult. Appearances are deceptive; many cases are known of two perfectly good species, each able to reproduce within its own group but not with the other, and yet no visible differences between the two. The name cryptic species applies where visible differences cannot be detected.

Perhaps the most widely held definition of species hinges on the matter of whether or not individuals under consideration can successfully interbreed. Thus a species is *a group of similar individuals which can interbreed and produce offspring that are in turn fertile with each other.* This is a practical definition but it does not take into account the great number of hybrids that are known, particularily among plants. Some hybrids exist for long time periods and are distinct from the parents that produced them. How much hybridization is permissible between parent species for these parents to be considered separate species?

Consider extinct species. Those who study fossils cannot apply the test of reproduction. What is left for study are mainly incomplete specimens. To the paleontologist a species must be an identifiable group that persists through time without fusing with some other group. This is a highly theoretical definition but it does call attention to the fact that species not only exist as living things but have a history in the past that must be taken into account. The great edifice of life is not a one-story building.

In a facetious but still serious way someone has said that a species is something that a reliable specialist has recently said is a species.

Anti-evolutionists have placed a great deal of emphasis on the crossing of animals and plants one with another. They take the phrase "after his kind" to mean that nothing that can cross with something else is a distinct kind. Since many species do cross, particularly among plants and lower animals, the anti-evolutionists are reluctant to accept species as equivalent to kinds. Even genra (next highest category above species) also cross and are thus eliminated as being the scriptural kinds. So one must go to a higher category still. It is at the family level where everyone feels fairly safe that there is no crossing. Consequently anti-evolutionists have taken a fairly strong stand that the biologist's family is the scriptural kind.

The endless and largely fruitless entanglements with the meaning of words that is illustrated in the above paragraphs should convince almost anyone of the absurdity of trying to place a restrictive technical meaning on what was intended to be a general term. All difficulties are swept away if we accept a definition of kind as being anything that reproduces successfully. A kind might then be a species, a genus, a family or even something broader. It might also be something less than a species such as a variety or a race; even hybrids would not be excluded. A kind could be a simple sexless bacteria, an organism with alternations of generations, a plant that propagates by branching or budding, and so upward to those higher things which produce fertilized eggs and living young.

What About Fossils?

In seeking ways to prove the literal truth of the scriptures creationists have found what they consider to be a great and fatal weakness in the evolutionist argument. Their point of attack is the imperfection of the fossil record of past life. The argument is this: evolution teaches that all species must be derived from previous species but the fossil record fails to supply the necessary stages in the postulated family trees.

According to strict creationism only divine intervention can produce the original kinds of plants and animals. Evolutionists believe that all levels of living things are produced by naturally occurring changes in the genes. The argument can be simplified to the question of the reality of the so-called "missing links." Creationists say these links never existed and hence will never be found; evolutionists say they did exist and may or may not be found. Since the supposed or actual appearance of most species must have taken place in the distant past the only place to look for the necessary evidence is in the fossil record. Creationists point out that the links required by evolutionists have not come to light in spite of decades of diligent search by those who sincerely wish to find them. Furthermore the claim is that entirely hypothetical forms are introduced on a wholesale basis to fill the gaps. Evolutionists reply that many good links have already been found and that fossilization, being a very haphazard process, cannot be expected to supply a complete and perfect record of all beings that lived in the past. The key question becomes, just how good or how bad is the fossil record. Some students regard it as surprisingly good, others as woefully bad; everyone wishes it could be better. The paleontologists have found enough to encourage them to keep digging and they seldom come home empty handed. Whatever else may be said about the fossil record it must always improve.

Anyone who thinks about the problem should contemplate the hazards that determine the fate of any products of the past. Consider the works and bodies of men. It is known that Rome was a city of millions of inhabitants—how many skeletons of those millions that lived only two thousand years ago are now to be found? And how many Athenians, or Alexandrians, or Babylonians? What is preserved of most ancient civilizations are things more durable than flesh and bone. Were it not for monuments of stone and artifacts of baked clay, metal and glass we would know but little of many great cultures of the past. Of the primitive nomadic tribes that once roamed North America the only really plentiful traces are arrow and spear points of stone. One might suppose that these durable objects were all that these ancient people made or possessed. And where would one go to find specimens of the bison that roamed the plains by millions along with the makers of the lances and arrows?

There are exceptions to the general scarcity of relics of human history and these are of great importance. Artifacts of the Egyptian civilization which flourished in a dry climate are relatively abundant. Here are objects of wood, papyrus, and fiber along with those of stone. Then too the practice of embalming has preserved hundreds of human bodies that would have otherwise gone the way of all flesh.

Critics of the pre-human or prehistoric record should honestly try to be realistic about the state of the fossil record. What can be expected to remain of living things after the passage of thousands, millions, hundreds of millions, even billions of years? Consider that to become a fossil, a dinosaur, for example, must have been buried immediately after death, petrified or otherwise preserved from decay as it lies within the earth, protected from the destructive effects of extreme heat and pressure, exposed at the proper time by erosion without being disintegrated by soil-forming processes, and finally, at the last minute rescued by an intelligent human being with the interest and knowledge to reconstruct and study it. Small wonder that those who have considered the matter would conclude that for every fossil known, literally thousands or tens of thousands once existed and have disappeared without a trace.

As with human remains and artifacts there are exceptions to the general scarcity of plant and animal fossils. When conditions are right, a fairly complete sample of the life of particular areas is buried and preserved. The famous Tar Pits of Los Angeles is a good example. Here in addition to the large and spectacular mammals there are many smaller ones, together with birds, reptiles, and amphibians. There are numerous insects and a variety of plants including large trees. All the forms that are found together constitute a unified, natural assemblage compatible with a specific climate and topographic setting. Fairly complete and balanced groups of fossil organisms have come to light at practically all levels of the past. It is to these that the student of evolution turns for much of his evidence. Like King Tutankhamun's tomb they throw light on certain times that far surpasses the general run of evidence.

Another truth should be born in mind. Someone said it well: *The beginnings of all things are small.* In every lineage of living things no matter how fragmentary it may be the earliest members are small; thus, small shellfish, small reptiles, including small dinosaurs, small horses and small monkeys. As one would expect, a small thing is less likely to be preserved than a large one. Not only were the first members of the individual lineages small in size but they were small in numbers. No matter what one may believe about the origins of any group it is contrary to all evidence, even scriptural, to suppose that it started with a large number of identical things. At first there were a few, then if these proved succesful, natural increase would bring larger numbers. Human experience verifies this, at first there were only a few Romans, or a few Americans— later there were millions.

These are the reasons why many critical links have not been and may never be found. It is in the transition from one group to another that the fossil record is weak and on this point the creationists have concentrated their attack. This is excellent tactics. No matter how many links are found there will be many still missing. Only when each creature of the past can come forth with a birth certificate attached can a die-hard critic be fully convinced.

Genetics—Each After His Kind

A complete history of biology might be written in terms of the gradual discovery of how reproduction of living things is accomplished. Much of a practical nature was known in prehistoric time; both plants and animals were domesticated and the production of certain desirable types was insured by selective breeding of animals and the collection, preservation and planting of superior seeds. Eggs, sperm and seeds were known to act in some mysterious way to carry the essence of inheritance but even Charles Darwin was far from the truth in his understanding of how it all operates.

Cells were discovered in 1665 by Robert Hooke but the theory that all living things consist of cells was not published until 1838. Shortly thereafter, in 1845, von Siebold declared that protozoa are simply animals that consist of single cells. Rudolf Virchow asserted that all cells must come from previous cells. Cell division and multiplication constitute an observable manifestation of reproduction and with the discovery of the minute threadlike chromosomes in the nucleus of cells during the 1870's the relation of cell division to the reproduction of the complete organism began to unfold. Next came the discovery in the period 1910-1920 that chromosomes consist of still smaller entities which were called genes and that these are the bearers of unit hereditary traits.

Attention then shifted from purely descriptive and observational matters to the physical and chemical bases of inheritance. Careful research established the fact that a remarkable substance in the nucleus of the cell called deoxyribonucleic acid or DNA is the ultimate hereditary determiner. The discovery of the composition and structure of DNA in 1953 may be the crowning contribution of biology. With the discovery of the famed double helix and the manner in which it replicates itself came the realization of what must precede the division of all cells and what ultimately carries the essence of inheritance from one generation to the next. No matter which of many means of reproduction an organism may depend on, the replication of DNA within it is basic. This is what assures that all things multiply after their kind.

Mankind consists of males and females and the well-known sexual processes of human reproduction may obscure the fact that there are many other very effective ways in which lesser beings perpetuate themselves. Everyone with an elemental knowledge of hygiene is familiar with diseases brought on by viruses, bacteria and protozoans. Viruses are the most simple, they consist of little more than the DNA and accompanying RNA needed to reproduce but they must get inside the cells they infect in order to multiply. Bacterial diseases are caused by the multiplication of entire cells, the same is true of the protozoan infections. The reproduction of single-celled organisms that cause disease differs in no essential way from that of their numerous harmless relatives. The basis for their multiplication is the division of the genetic material followed by the splitting of the cell. Cells may split lengthwise or crosswise or by breaking into a number of equal parts. Yeast cells, employed by man to create carbon dioxide in making bread, divide rapidly into numerous bud-like reproductions of the original. All these methods are said to be asexual as there is no difference between the products of reproduction.

The asexual method of reproduction also carries through hundreds of types of many-celled organisms. Budding is common, new individuals begin as branches or buds from the parent. The repulsive tapeworm may break into segments and each segment can become a new individual. From creeping lateral growths (stolons) new strawberry plants spring up to become separate from the parent when the stolon disintegrates.

Spores too are asexual. They are exceedingly small and dust-like and may be dispersed in water or air. Each is capable of becoming a new individual. Thousands of plants reproduce in this manner. It is their very smallness that enables them to spread widely but no matter how small they are the genetic material inside is complete. One more method of asexual reproduction that deserves mention is parthenogenesis. Here an unfertilized egg of a normally sexual type of organism is somehow stimulated to give rise to a complete individual.

Sexual reproduction has many advantages and is the method of the higher plants and animals. Here two individuals, generally termed male and female, must join or in some way exchange genetic material. Sperms and eggs are usually but not necessarily involved. Lowly plants and animals show the beginnings of sex when they exchange genetic material in the process of partial fusion or conjugation. Complete fusion is called syngamy.

The most successful forms of sexual reproduction involve the specialization of two sexual elements (gametes), one small and motile, the other larger and well supplied with nutrient. The former are called sperms, the latter eggs. In plants the eggs usually remain attached to the parent while the sperm must be transported in one way or another to reach the egg. Thus the pollen of plants may be carried by water, by air currents and by insects or larger animals. Examples are known to every observant person.

Animals must, in effect, solve the same problem as the plants in bringing together the male and female gametes. Those with external fertilization have instincts and methods for releasing the sexual products near each other, generally in water but this method is extremely wasteful. A female codfish is known to produce 6,000,000 eggs in a single season; not all of these are properly fertilized and of these in turn only a very small fraction become adult fish. Internal fertilization is clearly less wasteful. Here the eggs and sperms are placed in close proximity so that fertilization is generally assured without waste. Small wonder that two very successful groups of animals, insects and mammals, employ this method.

The many complicated processes and behavior patterns that bring about the mixing of genetic material cannot be discussed further. They are described in any good biology text. Many other topics must also be passed over lightly. One of these, called polyploidy is extremely important in producing new varieties of plants. It is a condition in which three or more complete sets of chromosomes are present in each cell. This multiplication of genetic material arises spontaneously and gives rise to plant types that are mutually fertile with each other but not with the parent from which they arose. Perhaps over one-third of the flowering plants have had this origin. The intricate subject of hybridization is one of great significance in horticulture and animal husbandry. Hybrids may be looked at as proving that the genetic material is both stable and plastic. It was with hybirds that Mendel proved the inheritance of unit characters. Where would the human race be without proper attention to the hybrids that have appeared naturally or been induced artificially in plants and animals? Grafting, which seems to have been practiced since ancient times, is yet another process that shows the importance of the genetic material. The desired characters are carried in the twigs or buds that are grafted onto stock with less desirable traits. In the terminal cells of the grafts is the material that will grow and produce what is wanted.

Finally to be mentioned is the process of cloning, a modern laboratory discovery. Every single cell of a carrot root or a tobacco plant stem can be isolated and will develop into an entire and perfect plant. These experiments show that the entire hereditary information needed for a new organism is contained in a single body cell. This opens up vast areas of speculation; many science-fiction plots have been based on the possibility that clones of human beings can be created. Here is even a believable analogy of the way that God could have created Eve from a "rib" of Adam.

Several fundamental truths emerge from what has been discovered about the reproduction and inheritance of living things. Perhaps most important is that there is a unity and continuity of life from its lowest to highest forms. All life, from bacterium to man, has DNA and RNA composed of a few basic molecules. The almost infinite variety of species is due only to the ways in which a few basic components called nucleotides are arranged. This chemical and structural similarity of the genetic material implies a common origin and subsequent extensive branching of life from one or a few simple beginnings. There is no good reason to suppose that the organisms of past geologic ages were in any way different in their reproductive mechanisms from their living descendants today.

The expression "each after his kind" is an excellent way of saying that each and every organism must develop according to the store of genetic material it receives from its parent or parents. One may or may not read into this the possibility of variations along the way but nature and scripture agree in this—there is no other way except by inheritance from ones own kind that anything can reproduce. No matter what else may be said, the very fact that nature displays her most intricate designs and subtle processes in connection with reproduction proves the importance of passing on undamaged genetic material from parent to offspring at all costs. I for one prefer to believe that this is the profound truth intended by the statement "each after his kind." Those who believe that this phrase serves only to warn us that species must never evolve should consider whether or not they are getting the entire message.

Comments and References

Two statements of Genesis pertain to the populating of the earth by living things. The first of these, mentioned in Genesis 1:11 and repeated several times thereafter specifies that both plants and animals reproduce "after their kind." The second, mentioned for the first time in Genesis 1:22 is that they should "multiply" and fill the waters and earth. It is true that these directives are not repeated in connection with every division of life but the implication is that they are intended for all things. Both are very basic and closely related but for purposes of discussion the statement "after their kind" has been considered first.

Those who think in terms of literal translations have taken the position that any and all things were made by God to reproduce without deviations throughout time with no mixing, crossing, or evolution whatsoever. In fact the phrase "after his kind" has become the chief text of anti-evolution and much has been written to prove that "kinds" do not and cannot cross with other kinds and do not give rise to anything different from the original kind brought forth in the beginning.

Granted that the term "after his kind" may be defended as anti-evolutionary one cannot help wondering if a more productive and scientific meaning might have been intended. Consider this: no living thing in the experience of man has ever come forth without parents or forebears from which it has derived the genetic material that makes it what it is. Ancient people knew nothing about chromosomes and DNA but we know today that genetic material is what *must* pass from parent to offspring and is what determines that no living thing can come in any other way than "after its kind." This is a fruitful thought because it can be tested by study of organisms at all levels of complexity.

The ways in which offspring are produced are amazingly varied and the subject is a profound one. All modern biology textbooks discuss reproduction. The subject is treated on a college level by C. A. Villee, *Biology,* Saunders; C. G. Simpson, C. S. Pittendrig, and L. H. Tiffany, 1957, *Life: An Introduction to Biology,* Harcourt, Brace; and W. T. Keeton, 1972, *Biological Science,* 2nd ed., W. W. Norton. No single book dealing with all methods by which "kinds" reproduce appears to have been written.

Those interested in the development of knowledge of genetics and genetic material will find the following books informative: Hans Stubbe, 1973, *History of Genetics* (translated by E. J. R. Waters), M.I.T. Press; Robert Olby, 1974, *The Path of the Double Helix,* University of Washington Press; and Franklyn H. Portugal and Jack S. Cohen, 1977, *A Century of DNA: A History of the Discovery of the Structure and Function of the Genetic Substance,* M.I.T. Press. A short semi-popular article, The New Genetics: The Threads of Life, by George W. Beadle appears in the 1964 *Encyclopedia Britannica Book of the Year.* Another excellent 3-part article under the title, The New Biology, is found in *The National Geographic Magazine,* September 1976.

25

Be Fruitful...Multiply...Fill the Waters

And God blessed them, saying, Be fruitful, and multiply, and fill the waters in the seas, and let fowl multiply in the earth.

Genesis 1:22

And I, God, blessed them, saying: Be fruitful, and multiply, and fill the waters in the sea; and let fowl multiply in the earth;...

Moses 2:22

And the Gods said: We will bless them, and cause them to be fruitful and multiply, and fill the waters in the seas or great waters; and cause the fowl to multiply in the earth.

Abraham 4:22

Here as in all matters relating to the creation of living things the accounts given in Genesis and Moses speak of God's decrees as though they took effect in the very day or period in which they were proclaimed. Abraham, however, makes clear that fulfillment is to be at a future time—we *will* bless them, not, we do now bless them. This is only reasonable, for why would anything be blessed that was not yet in existence?

The terminology "be fruitful and multiply" is repeated in connection with mankind: "And God blessed them and said unto them, *Be fruitful and multiply and replenish the earth,* and subdue it...." (Genesis 1:28.) Still later, after the flood, it is recorded that God instructed Noah:

Bring forth with thee every living thing that is with thee, of all flesh, both of fowl, and of cattle, and of every creeping thing that creepeth upon the earth; that they may breed abundantly in the earth, and be fruitful, and multiply upon the earth.

Genesis 8:17

One is almost inclined to ask why God should have found it necessary to command any living thing to multiply and be fruitful. Powerful inner drives would seem to make such a command unnecessary. Ask any student of biology to state in one phrase the most universal law of existence among living things and he must certainly reply: self preservation. From the simple escape reactions of an amoeba to the reasoned efforts of a human being the urge to remain alive is basic. Although preservation of the individual is often considered to be a matter separate from preservation of the race the distinction, in the end, is almost meaningless. One without the other is of no avail. Compared with the urge to reproduce and the urge to maintain the self all other struggles are minor. The existence of any animal must be short indeed if it put forth no efforts to maintain life and one brief generation is all that could possibly result if there were no inborn urge to reproduce.

The struggle to survive brings into use all the many devices and reactions which living things possess. That these devices and reactions exist in endless and marvelous variety is explained by some as a result of evolution, by others as an expression of the benevolence of God. Probably nothing separates believers in God from non-believers more neatly than their attitude on the problem of how plants and animals came to be suited for their varied modes and places of existence. The Creationist says simply and positively that living things were designed and brought forth by God in possession of everything needful for their existence. The Evolutionist says that organisms are modified by reactions between their environments of life and the genetic material within their bodies. Extreme creationism requires God to give personal attention to every species; extreme evolutionism requires no God at all. How unfortunate that in their zeal to promote one argument or the other the possibility of a reasonable compromise is seldom considered by the antagonists. Perhaps more consideration should be given to the basic scriptures. Do they really prohibit evolution and require strict creationism? Certainly they were given with serious intent. What was that intent?

When the scriptures say "multiply and replenish" do they mean that each species is to carry out the difficult tasks of self preservation and racial propagation with only the original allotment of capabilities? Or do scriptures allow the possibility that an original pattern might be altered with time to meet new situations as they inevitably arise? The wording itself does not specify one or the other. Perhaps the Parable of the Talents may have meaning here. He who made no efforts to improve or build upon his original gifts lost everything. So it seems to have been in nature. Species that have not adapted are dead. Yes, "dead as a dinosaur," has become a reference to those things which are outmoded and extinct. And consider what is known about the genes, those marvelous devices that shape the individual and carry traits of all kinds from one generation to the next. They seem to be constructed along very rigid lines and yet can be altered in both beneficial and harmful ways. This possibility of altering the genetic material is a fact of nature, but strict creationists do not admit that alterations, no matter how long continued, or added upon, are able to produce new "kinds" from old kinds. This topic is discussed at greater length at an appropriate place in the chapter "After His Kind."

One reason many religious persons have difficulty in accepting Darwin's theory of evolution is that constant deadly struggle is at the heart of it. Scientists may describe the fight for life in terms such as "natural selection," and "survival of the fittest" but the fact remains that death in all its varied forms is an essential ingredient. This is upsetting to those who believe in a loving beneficent Creator. Nevertheless, everyone, no matter what his religious beliefs may be, should be reminded that the struggle for existence is a fact of nature and Charles Darwin merely put it into a reasonable perspective.

Darwin arrived at a logical explanation for fossils and for the widespread waste of life when he considered two obvious facts of nature. The first of these is an over-production of individuals in all species. This means that many more seeds, spores, eggs, embryos and young individuals are produced than can ever reach adulthood. One species of fern can yield 30 million spores in one season and an ordinary corn plant sends forth 18 million pollen grains during its reproductive cycle. A single fish can spawn as many as 120 million eggs and a female frog lays about 20,000 eggs every year. It has been calculated that if all the offspring of a single pair of flies remained alive and reproduced at an ordinary rate, they would produce a mass of flies as large as the earth in a matter of only a few years.

Since only a relatively few of the plants and animals started in life ever reach a stage where they in turn can reproduce the obvious fate of most individuals is death. Many die without a struggle; seeds do not struggle, they fall, as well described in the Parable of the Sower, on all types of soil where only a few survive. Likewise eggs are totally defenseless and are sought out and devoured by countless hungry enemies. The struggle never lets up; at every stage of existence an animal or plant is subject to passive or active aggression by others of its own and other species and to perils brought on by the non-living forces of nature.

No measure of soft-hearted sentimentality can lessen the fact of a vast waste of life that goes on everywhere among all living things. Furthermore death is brought about by every conceivable means, starvation, disease, predation, and out-and-out bloody combat between and within species. The means may seem repulsive and unworthy of God but it is evidently the results that count. Let those who think in theological terms explain the sufferings of men, the salvation of the good and the damnation of the bad as they criticize the concept of the survival of the fittest in the natural world.

These are grim thoughts but the directive to "multiply and replenish" would seem to lead inevitably to struggle and competition. As Malthius pointed out, the resources of the earth are limited while the power to reproduce is not. Consequently nothing can multiply unopposed. Some must give way, many must die. To borrow a phrase: Many are called but few are chose. The thought is a good one for evolutionists as well as creationists.

Comments and References

The subject of biological reproduction was discussed in chapter 24 in connection with the "after his kind" biblical texts. How reproduction takes place is no longer a mystery and why offspring resemble their parents is now explained in a natural way. These factual matters can be thought of as a field entirely separate from organic evolution. That individuals are born, grow and die is known to even the most ignorant and unlearned; that species appear, develop, and disappear is much less apparent but no less real. The difference is one of time and human perspective. Individual lives are short, racial lives are so long that they are not comprehensible without taking into account the evidence of fossils and the long-term implications of genetics. Again the subject is vast and to the non-specialist, utterly bewildering. This chapter is an attempt to justify the thought that the command, admonition and blessing to multiply and replenish the earth applies to more than day-to-day reproduction. It clearly seems to do more than merely approve the idea of organic evolution. In the end the creation of new species appears to be the way that life has multiplied and filled the earth.

The topic of evolution was introduced in chapter 22 in connection with the origin of life; references given there were not intended to enlarge on the subject of what happened after life got under way. Looking ahead, the origin and evolution of man will be treated in chapters 29 and 30. Again the references do not cover the subject of organic evolution as a general process.

For those willing to give the controversial subject of organic evolution a fair hearing the best place to commence is the classical book by Charles Darwin, *"On the Origin of Species by Means of Natural Selection or the Preservation of Favored Races in the Struggle for Life,"* published in 1859. There have been numerous editions and the book is widely available. From this basic beginning the field widens and the choices are difficult. A widely recommended but slightly outdated book is G. G. Simpson, 1953, *The Major Features of Evolution,* Columbia University Press. Probably nothing ever produced in popular printed form exceeds in total impact the series entitled The World We Live In issued by Life Magazine in the interval December 8, 1952 to December 20, 1954. The 13 parts of the series were reissued in a book of the same title by Time Incorporated in 1955. In the articles and book the succession of life is discussed and illustrated with special emphasis on the Age of Reptiles and Age of Mammals; the illustrations are as authentic as it is possible to achieve. A second book, *The Wonders of Life on Earth* was issued by Time Incorporated in 1960. It too is lavishly illustrated and in reality is an updated commentary on the research and contributions of Charles Darwin.

Another widely available reference is the Life Nature Library, a series of 18 volumes by recognized authorities issued by Time Incorporated. The diversity of life is emphasized. The volume titled *Evolution* issued in 1964 is particularly informative. Another set of books from the same source is the Emergence of Man Library; the volume *Life Before Man,* 1972, gives the evolutionary background of man. Other than this the remaining volumes treat the progress of man as man. Probably the best survey of the fossil evidence is *Evolution and the Fossil Record,* a selection of papers from the Scientific American with an introduction by Leo F. Laporte, Freeman, 1978. The entire September 1978 issue of Scientific American is devoted to the subject of organic evolution. This is essentially the latest (not last) word on the subject.

Those who find the concept of organic evolution unacceptable should study the writings of creationists. Many books, pamphlets, tapes and courses of study are available from Creation-Life Publishers, P.O. Box 15666, San Diego, California 92115.

26

Behold It Was Very Good

"And God saw every thing that he had made, and, behold, it was very good. And the evening and the morning were the sixth day."

Genesis 1:31

"And I, God, saw everything that I had made, and, behold, all things which I had made were very good; and the evening and the morning were the sixth day."

Moses 3:31

(The Book of Abraham has no parallel passage on this topic.)

It would be surprising if God should declare his creations anything but good. What is surprising is that man frequently judges these same creations to be bad. The theological explanation usually given is that the creations of God were perfectly good to begin with and that the badness that now exists is due to the Fall of Adam and other signs of mankind. In the minds of many this places on Adam the blame for everything that isn't to their liking. The "thorns and thistles" that sprang up to torment and afflict man were accompanied by endless other evils such as mosquitoes, rattlesnakes, and bubonic plague. The contrast between the original goodness of creation and the present imperfect state of the world reaches its extreme expression in the so-called "no death before the Fall" doctrine which is held by some theologians. According to this idea the world before the Fall was not only perfect in every sense it was also free of death. Nothing was dying, each individual plant and animal continued in its original perfection without reproduction until the curse of Adam fell upon it. Yes, Adam's transgression brought death into the world not only for himself and his descendants but also for all other living things! Most churches do not go this far but by interpreting the scriptures in literal ways they manage to throw on Adam and Eve most of the blame for everything that they consider to be wrong with the earth and mankind.

Books have been written on how sin originated, how it changed the world and how original perfection has deteriorated to present imperfection. Only a few additional comments in connection with the topic of creation can be given here. In the first place, it was God who pronounced his creations good and we must certainly grant that he knows better than we do what is good and what is not. That which is satisfactory or excellent in our selfish human, earth-centered view may not be good in the eternal, heaven-centered view of God, the Creator. Like children, it is doubtful we know what is really good for ourselves let alone for any greater purposes.

When God revealed to Moses the creation of this and other worlds, he disclosed the ultimate purpose thus: "For behold, this is my work and my glory—to bring to pass the immortality and eternal life of man." (Moses 1:39.) This declared objective of God has been manifest in every detail and its essentials made known to man from the beginning in the form of the plan of salvation. It is a step-by-step program which if followed is one of eternal progression. Might we not presume that anything that contributes to the successful carrying out of this plan is good in the sight of God? Consider this scripture which reveals one essential step in the plan:

> "...We will go down, for there is space there, and we will take of these materials, and we will make an earth whereon these may dwell;
> And we will prove them herewith, to see if they will do all things whatsoever the Lord their God shall command them;
> And they who keep their first estate shall be added upon; and they who keep not their first estate shall not have glory in the same kingdom with those who keep their first estate; and they who keep their second estate shall have glory added upon their heads for ever and ever."
> Abraham 4:24-26

An earth and an earth-life are clearly essential to the carrying out of the plan of salvation. Furthermore, the earth was planned to be a testing or proving place. It is a demonstrated fact of human existence that nothing is proved or tested without trial and opposition. Consider this from the Book of Mormon:

"...for there is a God, and he hath created all things, both the heavens and the earth, and all things that in them are, both things to act and things to be acted upon.

And to bring about his eternal purposes in the end of man, after he had created our first parents, and the beasts of the field and the fowls of the air, and in fine, all things which are created, it must needs be that there was an opposition; even the forbidden fruit in opposition to the tree of life; the one being sweet and the other bitter.

Wherefore, the Lord God gave unto man that he should act for himself. Wherefore, man could not act for himself save it should be that he was enticed by the one or the other.

2 Nephi 2:14-16

Only a childish mind would want to live in a world without challenge, opposition and trial. Shakespeare wrote: "For as you know security is mortals' chiefest enemy."

The essence of Darwinian evolution is survival of the fittest; living things with or without man are to the biologist largely the outcome of ages of trial, endless struggle and ruthless elimination of the unfit. The impersonal, unthinking forces of nature bring trials to every living thing. Man to a large extent can avoid the trials of lesser beings but he can conscientiously choose to undergo trials of a higher nature. He can embark willingly upon programs of self-improvement including the greatest of all, enlistment in the plan of salvation.

What was the status of things when they were pronounced good? The clue is that the declaration was made at the end of the sixth day, not in the seventh day. Consider that "there was not yet flesh upon the earth, neither in the water, neither in the air." Man was not here—his physical creation is distinctly an event of the seventh day. Considering also that it had not yet rained upon the earth, it is inconceivable that land vegetation could have been in existence. The earth was apparently lifeless, barren and uninhabited by any higher forms of life. Yet God pronounced it good! Earth was certainly far from being a paradise in any human sense at this stage of existence but it had the potential of becoming one. Clearly, that which man considers good and beautiful is less basic and important than that which will later become good and beautiful.

The wisdom, might, power, and intelligence of God is shown more abundantly in the establishment of a system that was bound to succeed than it could possibly be by any series of mighty works that had to be imposed upon an imperfect system already in existence. As long as man equates his works such as the building of dams, the digging of canals and the planting of fields with the creative works of God he will never appreciate what God has done or how it was accomplished. I know of no more perceptive statement than that of Charles Kingsley:

"We know of old that God was so great that he could make all things, but behold He is so much greater even than that, that He can make all things make themselves."

Comments and References

The goodness of God's creations have inspired expressions of human praise and admiration throughout recorded history. Surely the greatest compliment to be paid a creator is to study his creations. It is the point of this chapter that God was satisfied and pleased with his efforts long before they bore fruit in the world as man knows it. That this is so is an undeniable indication of the relationship between Genesis 1 and Genesis 2 and the wisdom of the two accounts of creation.

An interesting chapter in the history of science and theology is the Bridgewater Treatises. A wish of Francis H. Egerton, eighth Earl of Bridgewater, who died in 1829, as expressed in his will, was to find and support eight scientific authors capable of demonstrating "the Power, Wisdom, and Goodness of God, as manifested in the Creation." Eight great volumes carrying out this wish were published in England between 1838 and 1870. As human statements for the goodness of God's ultimate creations, the Bridgewater Treatises are unsurpassed. However, their arguments have largely crumbled. Natural processes have proven perfectly capable of producing the effects which men have piously ascribed to God. It is by calling on divine or supernatural influences to explain that which may later be shown to be natural that well-meaning men have greatly weakened the concept of God as a creator. Modern creationists and fundamentalists would do well to study the arguments of their predecessors—and not repeat the fallacious ones.

The idea that all things can and do develop in inevitable or predestined ways is an old one in religion, philosophy, and science. A central aspect of Plato's philosophy is the division of the universe in two parts. Although he did not make the connection clear he saw a world of change and becoming on one hand and a world of eternal, immutable things on the other. The immutable things he called

"Ideas" or "Forms." Aristotle, student of Plato, and the greatest biologist of ancient time also recognized a distinction between the potential and the actual. In the seed and embryo he saw the possibility of the fully developed organism. In all things he distinguished "matter from form, the relatively raw stuff from the finished product." These philosophers were not, however, greatly concerned with the ultimate beginning of lineages or generations—they accepted man as man and not as a development from something less.

Science today portrays the universe, the earth, life in general and man in particular as having resulted from a long line of natural cause-and-effect events. This has been a great irony of history—the need for God as a supernatural creator has gradually faded away. Disillusionment and disappointment exist in spite of finding every aspect of creation amazing and awe inspiring, even faith promoting. The disappointment comes in finding no one along the line or behind the scenes producing the miracles that we had been told about and were expecting. To many the creator has become a "hydrogen god" or a "big bang god"—far too remote and impersonal to have concern for man.

Genesis, when properly understood, has the antidote for despair. The glory of God's creative power is that he knows and commands his materials so well that once they are organized the desired results must follow no matter how complex the process or long-delayed the outcome. Here, plainer than in any philosophy, is the demonstration that there are two levels of being, the potential and the actual.

27

On the Seventh Day God Ended His Work...and Rested

"And on the seventh day God ended his work which he had made; and he rested on the seventh day from all his work which he had made.

And God blessed the seventh day, and sanctified it: because that in it he had rested from all his work which God created and made."

Genesis 2:2-3

"And on the seventh day I, God, ended my work, and all things which I had made; and I rested on the seventh day from all my work, and all things which I had made were finished, and I, God, saw that they were good;

And I, God, blessed the seventh day, and sanctified it; because that in it I had rested from all my work which I, God, had created and made."

Moses 3:2-3

"And the Gods said among themselves: On the seventh time we will end our work, which we have counseled; and we will rest on the seventh time from all our work which we have counseled.

And the Gods concluded upon the seventh time, because that on the seventh time they would rest from all their works which they (the Gods) counseled among themselves to form; and sanctified it...."

Abraham 5:2-3

Christians learn from their Sunday School lessons that God created the earth in six days and rested on the seventh. The story is told in Genesis and emphasized a number of times in subsequent scripture. Exodus 20:11 states: "For in six days the Lord made

171

heaven and earth, the sea, and all that in them is, and rested the seventh day...." Hebrews 4:4 says: "For he spake in a certain place of the seventh day on this wise, and God did rest the seventh day from all his works."

Consider this statement from Moses, "And I, the Lord God, had created all the children of men; and not yet a man to till the ground; for in heaven created I them; and there was not yet flesh upon the earth, neither in the water, neither in the air;..." (Moses 3:5.) This is certainly a revealing but at the same time a confusing statement. How could God's work be complete as long as flesh of all kinds including especially man was still not present on earth? One gets the impression of a planet "desolate and void" as described at the beginning; scarcely a picture of a creation finished and complete.

Despite its unfinished condition and the absence of life, the earth was nevertheless almost ready to fill its appointed mission and God had pronounced it good at the end of the sixth day. All the preparations of earth and water were now to take effect. The scene was set for a significant and crucial event—the watering of the earth.

This is probably the best place to examine more closely the question of God's activities on the seventh day as contrasted with those of the previous days. The whole area has been one of misunderstanding and confusion chiefly because the nature of creation itself has been largely incomprehensible. A distinction is evidently to be made between the work of creation and other works of God. God is said to be resting on the seventh day. Note the exact words, God is resting "from all his work which God created and made." Again: "...on the seventh time they would rest from all their works which they (the Gods) counseled among themselves to form..." The Revised Standard Version of the Bible (1960) puts it thus: "...God rested from all his work which he had done in creation."

The topic of what constitutes God's work and also his rest has entered into arguments about the age of the earth and the duration of the seventh day. Some maintain that the seventh day isn't over. They argue that even after he had created Adam God did other works such as plant the Garden of Eden and write the 10 commandments for Moses.

If God is doing work of any kind, the argument continues, then he isn't resting and the seventh day cannot be over. Furthermore, the seventh day must be at least as long as it has been since it started approximately with the appearance of man 6,000 years ago. On the assumption that the 6,000 year period is nearing a close the end of the seventh day of creation is also at hand. In other words, when the seventh day is terminated, it will have been 6,000 years long. And if the seventh or last day is 6,000 years long, then each of the previous days were probably also that long, giving a total duration of the earth of 36,000 years. This is the belief and teaching of the Seventh Day Adventists if I understand it correctly.

On the other hand there are powerful scriptorians who profess that the seventh day *is* over. The argument is based on scriptures such as these, Genesis 2:2, "He (God) rested on the seventh day from all his work"; Exodus 20:11, "The Lord rested on the seventh day"; Genesis 2:3, "In it (the seventh day) he had rested. Finally, Hebrews 4:4, "God did rest the seventh day from all his works." All of these state that God rested on the seventh day, none says that he *is now* resting, therefore the rest period must be over. But note the entire and exact text:

> "And on the seventh day God ended his *work which he had made;* and he rested on the seventh day from all his work *which he had made.*
>
> "And God blessed the seventh day and sanctified it, because that in it he had rested from all his work *which God created and made."*
>
> Genesis 2:2-3

The scriptures do give a satisfactory answer to the problem of the seventh day. Several references including the one just cited tell exactly what it is that God had completed and from which he rested. That which was finished was that which had been "created and made" or simply that which God had made. Put in another way, after he pronounced things good he organized (or made) no more material in the creative sense. "Thus the heaven and the earth were finished, and all the host of them." (Genesis 2:1.) Note that this statement was made *before* the watering of the earth, *before* the appearance of flesh of any kind and *before* the coming of man.

Surely, God, being what he is, can and does do more than create. This is only one of his works. Does he not say, "This is my *work* and my glory, to bring to pass the immortality and eternal life of man." How could his work be over when men by the billions were yet to come to earth? An idle God is inconceivable and so is one who has withdrawn from the scene or lost interest in man.

Before scriptorians terminate the seventh day or put God in retirement they should consider where their arguments leave them. What is to be made of the fact that no mention is made of an eighth day either in ancient or modern revelations? This makes one very suspicious that no eighth day exists or is intended in the over all economy of God. By all interpretations the work of God in relation to man and this temporal earth is to be finished on the seventh day. The Book of Revelation which God gave to John "to shew unto his servants things which must shortly come to pass" describes in allegorical terms the events of the last days. It is replete with references to the number seven: seven churches, seven stars, seven last plagues, seven mountains, seven heads, seven eyes, seven horns, seven angels, etc.

One of the significant events of the last days is described thus:

> "And when the seven thunders had uttered their voices, I was about to write: and I heard a voice from heaven saying unto me, Seal up those things which the seven thunders uttered, and write them not.
>
> And the angel which I saw stand upon the sea and upon the earth lifted up his hand to heaven,
>
> And sware by him that liveth for ever and ever, who created heaven, and the things that therein are, and the earth, and the things that therein are, and the sea, and the things which are therein, that *there should be time no longer:...*"
>
> Revelation 10:4-6

Is the fact that time will come to an end the reason that there is no eighth day? Eternity is not divided into days. Time exists only when it is measured or measurable. This is the great distinction between time and eternity—time is measured, eternity is not. Consider this from the Book of Mormon: "...all is one day with God, and time only is measured unto men." (Alma 40:8.)

There is more; if we are still in the seventh day, how long has it already endured? The exact beginning of the seventh day is not specified, but it was marked approximately by the watering of the earth. This is an event that geologists are able to date with considerable assurance. Water produces sedimentary rocks, that is, rocks deposited in layers and consisting of worn fragments that collectively are called sand, silt, and gravel. Non-sedimentary rocks such as granite and basalt are produced by igneous action. No sedimentary rocks were found on the moon, igneous rocks are everywhere.

The oldest known rocks of the earth are of igneous types and are dated at almost 4 billion years. The first sedimentary rocks come somewhat later at about 3,500,000,000 years. The evidence is that somewhere between these two dates water appeared on the earth in sufficient quantity to fill oceans and create running streams.

I accept the approximate time of the arrival of water as given by geologists as three and one half billion years ago. On this assumption I base my argument that the seventh day is at least this long. In no other way can I reconcile God's statement that in the seventh day he not only concluded his creative work but also rested or ceased to create. This removes a great cause of contention between those who believe in creationism and those who believe in evolutionism. Creationists rightfully insist that God is the creator but they should realize that so far as this earth is concerned he is not now creating and has not been creating for a very long time by human standards. Evolutionists maintain, just as rightly, that they see no evidence of an ongoing creation in the natural world which they have been observing and studying in a scientific way. They must look farther back into the earlier six days of creation for evidences of the creative activity of God.

Faced with the fantastic, awe-inspiring phenomenon of the universe men have had to choose between belief that it runs itself with no need for a Creator and belief that it cannot run itself or exist without a Creator. Both views are possible because neither takes in the total view of things. They conflict for the same reason. There can be no reconciliation if evolutionists are not allowed time and space in which to fit their facts of observation, experience, and experimentation. Creationists, must likewise be given a place for the operation of an all-powerful God. In the totality of time and eternity and by the boundless wisdom of God both are possible.

The Age of the Earth

Some Latter-day Saint scholars have strongly supported the idea that a creation day is 1,000 years long. The chief basis for this belief is the reference to 1,000-year long days in the Book of Abraham:

"And I, Abraham, had the Urim and Thummim, which the Lord my God had given unto me, in Ur of the Chaldees;

And I saw the stars, that they were very great, and that one of them was nearest unto the throne of God; and there were many great ones which were near unto it;

And the Lord said unto me: These are the governing ones; and the name of the great one is Kolob, because it is near unto me, for I am the Lord thy God: I have set this one to govern all those which belong to the same order as that upon which thou standest.

And the Lord said unto me, by the Urim and Thummim, that Kolob was after the manner of the Lord, according to its times and seasons in the revolutions thereof; that one revolution was a day unto the Lord, after his manner of reckoning, it being one thousand years according to the time appointed unto that whereon thou standest. This is the reckoning of the Lord's time, according to the reckoning of Kolob."

Abraham 3:1-4

Again after the description of the creation and the placing of Adam in the Garden of Eden we read:

"And the Gods commanded the man, saying: Of every tree of the garden thou mayest freely eat,

But of the tree of knowledge of good and evil, thou shalt not eat of it; for in the time that thou eatest thereof, thou shalt surely die. Now I, Abraham, saw that it was after the Lord's time, which was after the time of Kolob; for as yet the Gods had not appointed unto Adam his reckoning.

Abraham 5:12-13

The reader has two choices in interpreting the phrase "it was after the Lord's time." Does *it* apply to the entire story of creation with the intention of setting a precise 1,000 year span on each of the six (or seven) days of creation? Or does it apply only to the admonition given to Adam and Eve in the very same sentence that if they transgressed, they would die in the same "time" that they did so eat, namely, within 1,000 years?

Believers in 1,000-year long creative days offer this scripture also:

"But, beloved, be not ignorant of this one thing, that one day is with the Lord as a thousand years, and a thousand years as one day."

II Peter 3:8

Again there would seem to be two possible interpretations. Both require the reader to supply what he considers to be the proper meaning. Those who would equate one day of God with a thousand years of man would have to supply the words in parenthesis—"That one day is with the Lord as a thousand years (with man) and a thousand years (with man) is as one day (with the Lord)." Those who might consider this verse merely as indicating that time has less meaning with God than with Man would supply the following parenthetical words—"That one day with the Lord is as a thousand years (with the Lord) and a thousand years (with the Lord) is as one day (with the Lord)."

Another scripture to be considered is this:

> "For a thousand years in thy sight is but as yesterday when it is past, and as a watch in the night."
>
> Psalm 90:4

And this:

> "And again, verily I say unto you, he hath given a law unto all things by which they move in their times and seasons;
> And their courses are fixed; even the courses of the heavens and the earth, which comprehend the earth and all the planets;
> And they give light to each other in their times and in their seasons, in their minutes, in their hours, in their days, in their weeks, in their months, in their years; *all these are one year with God, but not with man.*
>
> D & C 88:42-44

Certainly the phrase "a thousand years" is frequently used to designate a long time period without a real intent to be specific. Thus even today we frequently hear such expressions as "never in a thousand years." Students of scripture are apparently free to decide whether or not the creative periods were 24-hours, 1,000 years, or indefinite periods of greater length. Evidently in ancient times the concept of great numbers and long time periods were conveyed well enough by the words thousand and thousands; these words are found in about 450 verses in the King James translation. The word million, which is a more modern expression of largeness and greatness, occurs not at all in the King James Version, the word millions is found once.

Comments and References

The seventh day is a reality of biblical literature. All commentaries give space to it but emphasis and approaches differ from church to church. Most references to the seventh day are related to the Sabbath or Sunday, how these are celebrated, which day of the week is the seventh day, and events associated with it in history. It is surprising that the institution of a day of rest as a memorial to the rest of God after the works of creation is usually barely mentioned, seldom stressed.

The attitude that the seventh day is more of a convenience for man or perhaps even his invention than it is a serious reminder about the creation seems widespread. The Sabbath has certainly become more human-oriented and less God-oriented. Many historical and legalistic connotations of the Sabbath receive much more attention than does any thought that it tells some very profound things about the natural world.

The problem of whether or not we are still in the seventh day seems of little concern to bible students. In this book a central argument is that the seventh day is not over and that God's word is true and literal—he completed his creative works and has desisted from this type of effort since rains fell naturally upon the earth at the beginning of the seventh day a very long time ago.

Comments on the seventh day may be found in *The Interpreters Bible*, Vol. 1, p. 488-490; *The Encyclopedia Judaica*, Vol. 14, p. 558-573; *The New Catholic Encyclopedia*, Vol. 12, p. 778-782; *The Catholic Encyclopedia*, Vol. 4, p. 476-473; and *The Encyclopedia of Biblical Interpretation*, Vol. 1, p. 78-86. The last named reference seems to express all possible thoughts on the subject. Latter-day Saints will find a brief entry on the Sabbath in *Mormon Doctrine*, 1958 edition, p. 592.

28

A Mist From the Earth... Watered...the Ground

"But there went up a mist from the earth, and watered the whole face of the ground."

Genesis 2:6

"But I, the Lord God, spake, and there went up a mist from the earth, and watered the whole face of the ground."

Moses 3:6

"But there went up a mist from the earth, and watered the whole face of the ground."

Abraham 5:6

The watering of the ground as described in the above verses was a major turning point in the history of the earth. Apparently it is the first event of the seventh day and with it begins the "natural" existence of living things.

Plants and animals mentioned before the watering were in a spiritual or potential state and had not yet appeared on the earth. This is made abundantly clear in Moses 3:4:

"...For I, the Lord God, created *all things,* of which I have spoken, spiritually, before they were naturally upon the face of the earth. For I, the Lord God, had not caused it to rain upon the face of the earth. And I, the Lord God, had created all the children of men; and not yet a man to till the ground; for in heaven created I them; and there was not yet flesh upon the earth, neither in the water, neither in the air;..."

This quotation constitutes a most significant link between science and scripture, between Genesis and geology. Here we are told in a somewhat figurative but unmistakable way that the waters came out of the earth. The presence of water on the earth constitutes a great scientific problem. It is now fairly certain that none of the other planets of the solar system possess bodies of water; in the solar system the earth is unique in having abundant water in oceans, lakes, ice caps and atmosphere. About 300,000,000 cubic miles of liquid water exist on the surface of the globe which incidentally might well have been called Water and not Earth.

Where did the earth get its water in the first place and how has it been able to keep it for long periods of time? The answer involves a great deal of technical information and speculation that need not be given in detail here. Assume as an arbitrary starting point that the earth was once molten, completely melted from center to surface and of course, so hot that there could be no solid crust let alone bodies of water. In prescientific centuries it was assumed that all the water of the earth was once contained in a thick cloudy atmosphere. Any water that fell as rain would immediately evaporate and return to the clouds above. At this point we should note that only about 3,100 cubic miles of the earth's total water is in the atmosphere at any one time. The primitive atmosphere, if it really contained all the water now on the earth would have been incomparably more dense and extensive than the present one.

But the idea of all the water being in a primitive atmosphere is no longer in favor. A much better theory was proposed by the geologist, W. W. Rubey in 1952. In brief terms his theory proposes that the water that now exists on or near the earth's surface came from within its interior. The appearance of water at the surface was a direct consequence of cooling and solidification. The technical term for the process involved is "degassing"; this may be crudely compared to a stewing or cooking process. The essential elements for creating water are abundantly present within the earth perhaps in uncombined or disassociated form. This is shown by the continuous appearance of enormous quantities of water and water vapor from volcanoes, fumaroles, hot springs and geysers. All that is needed is plenty of time for enough water to come to the surface to fill the ocean basins and atmosphere. It is supposed that the rate of water production has been decreasing and that there was more volcanic action in the earlier stages of the earth's history.

Many lines of evidence indicate that Rubey's theory is at least on the right track. Common sense as well as good chemical theory tells us that a molten earth-sized body would be so hot that most gases including water vapor would be driven into space and lost forever. To escape from the earth a molecule of water vapor would have to attain a velocity of almost 3,700 feet per second. This velocity could easily be reached in association with a molten earth. Here, also is an explanation for the absence of water on the Moon and its scarcity on Mars. The escape velocity from the Moon is approximately 750 feet per second and is easily attained by any volatile material that is or has been there. Even though water may have been produced from the interior it would have escaped as soon as it appeared. Mars has an escape velocity of 1,600 feet per second and some water is retained. It is worth mentioning in passing that Jupiter has a layer or shell of water vapor in its atmosphere and water ice is probably present on Saturn.

The accumulation of water under the Rubey theory was a relatively slow process. This is significant in connection with the saltiness of the ocean. If one were to believe in the sudden production of the oceans as soon as rain could fall on a newly cooled earth it seems obvious that these water bodies would be relatively fresh. The salt would have to be added slowly as erosion of the land took place. The best evidence we have is that the oceans were salty from the beginning; as the water increased in volume salt was slowly added to keep the salinity about the same through time.

From the viewpoint of living things including man the most important event in the history of the earth was the appearance of water. Water in liquid form exists in exactly the same temperature range that living things can tolerate. This is only to be expected because protoplasm is about 80 percent water and an animal body such as that of man is about 75 percent water. The presence of water anywhere indicates that the temperature is right for life. We wouldn't expect to find life as we know it on planets either too hot or too cold for liquid water.

Geologists recognize another important effect of water. This is its essential role in producing the sedimentary rock record. In other words, the great class of rocks which results from deposition in water could not begin to form until water was present in large amounts. Igneous and metamorphic rocks were being formed from the beginning of the earth but not such water-laid varieties as sandstone, limestone, shale and coal. We can be assured that geologists can recognize the effects of water deposition in rocks of ancient origin. Such features as ripple marks, raindrop impressions, cross-bedding and concretions are sure accompaniments of water. Since most of these evidences require water in motion it is fairly certain that the same forces which now operate were operating then to lift water vapor into the atmosphere and to cause its condensation and precipitation so that it could flow downward by gravity in streams toward permanent oceans and seas. This is the great hydrologic or water cycle of the earth.

Important indeed was the appearance of water; without it life could not exist on earth and the surface of the planet would resemble that of the Moon or Mars. It is not to be wondered that geologists are very interested in finding the oldest sedimentary rocks as a sign of water action. And it is likewise not unremarkable that it is in these very old rocks that the first simple beginnings of life are found.

The earliest known water-laid sediments are dated at about three billion, three hundred million years old. These ancient rocks are the Fig Tree Series found in South Africa. Although other sedimentary rocks older than these may yet be found it is pointed out by geologists that few areas of the earth remain to be explored where such old rocks could be located.

Here is the important scriptural connection. If the watering of the earth took place over three billion years ago and we are still in the seventh day, then the seventh day is already over 3 billion years long. Presumably this final day will close with the "end of the earth" at some indefinite time in the future. This raises the interesting problem of whether or not there are more than seven days in God's plans concerning this earth.

Comments and References

This chapter deals specifically with the origin of the surface water of the earth. The very important paper by W. W. Rubey to which reference is made in the text is: Geologic History of Sea Water: An Attempt to State the Problem: *Geological Society of America Bulletin,* Vol. 62, p. 1111-1147, 1951. A follow-up paper in the same technical vein is by H. D. Holland, 1972, The Geologic History of Sea Water—An Attempt to Solve the Problem, *Geochimica et Cosmochimica Acta,* Vol. 36, p. 637-651.

An excellent look on the origin of water and related topics is: P. J. Brancazio and A. G. W. Cameron (eds.), 1964, *The Origin and Evolution of Atmosphere and Oceans,* John Wiley and Sons. Also up-to-date and informative is James C. G. Walker, 1977, *Evolution of the Atmosphere,* Macmillan Publishing Co.

Water as a substance essential to life is discussed in a nontechnical way in the Yearbook of the U.S. Department of Agriculture for 1955. Titled simply *Water,* this book shows the vital influence of water in human affairs. A popular prize-winning discussion of the greatest water-body of earth is Rachel L. Carson, 1961, *The Sea Around Us* (rev. ed.), Oxford University Press.

29

Of...Dust...the Breath of Life... Man Became a Living Soul

"And the Lord God formed man of the dust of the ground, and breathed into his nostrils the breath of life; and man became a living soul."

Genesis 2:7

"And I, the Lord God, formed man from the dust of the ground, and breathed into his nostrils the breath of life; and man became a living soul,..."

Moses 3:7

"And the Gods formed man from the dust of the ground, and took his spirit (that is, the man's spirit), and put it into him; and breathed into his nostrils the breath of life, and man became a living soul.

Abraham 5:7

No single subject has so baffled and frustrated man as his attempts to define himself. Is he an exhalted beast or a fallen angel? The Psalmist asks: What is man...? And there must be at least part of an answer in Paul's first epistle to the Corinthians:

"...There is a natural body, and there is a spiritual body.

And so it is written, The first man Adam was made a living soul; and the last Adam was made a quickening spirit.

Howbeit that was not first which is spiritual, but that which is natural; and afterward that which is spiritual.

The first man is of the earth, earthly: the second man is the Lord from heaven."

1 Corinthians 15:44-47

The creation scripture gives two accounts of the coming forth of man. The texts which open this chapter describe the appearance of the specific man Adam on the seventh day. It may be well to recall for comparison and contrast what is said in the account of the previous or sixth day. This describes the preparations for man and speaks of him in a general way only:

"So God created man in his own image, in the image of God created he him; male and female created he them."

Genesis 1:27

"And I, God, created man in mine own image, in the image of mine Only Begotten created I him; male and female created I them."

Moses 2:27

"So the Gods went down to organize man in their own image, in the image of the Gods to form they him, male and female to form they them."

Abraham 4:27

The sixth-day description is important and revealing but it is the seventh day narrative that is of concern at this point. Here, the dual nature of man is emphasized particularly in Abraham which makes clear beyond doubt that there is a physical man, the entity formed from the dust of the ground and a spiritual man, the spirit that was put into the physical body so that the totality became a living soul. Latter-day Saints should never forget this simple scripture: "And the spirit and the body are the soul of man." (D&C 88:15.) James E. Talmage gives this important comment:

"In speaking of the origin of man we generally have reference to the creation of man's body; and of all the mistakes that man has made concerning himself, one of the greatest and the gravest is that of mistaking the body for the man. The body is no more truly the whole man than the coat the body. The man, as an individual intelligence existed before his earthly body was framed and shall exist after that body has suffered dissolution. Let it not be assumed that belief in the existence of man's spirit is a conception founded upon scriptural authority only, on the contrary, let it be known, that it is in accordance with the best and most advanced scientific thought and philosophic belief of the day to hold that man consists of spirit and body; and Divine revelation makes plain that these together constitute the soul."

From *The Earth and Man*, Deseret News, November 21, 1931.

Consider the origin of the body of man—the entity made from the dust on the seventh day. It is somewhat surprising that the familiar phrase "dust of the earth" is not found in these scriptures—instead all three use the phrase "dust of the ground." Ground seems to be a better word than earth because as used elsewhere in Genesis it conveys a very good mental image of what men and living things generally are really made of.

Note the usage of Genesis 2:6 which describes the mist which "...watered the whole face of the ground." This is followed immediately by the planting of the garden of Eden, implying, it would seem, that it is the soil that men cultivate that is important here. And we are informed very soon in verse 9 that "...out of the ground made the Lord God to grow every tree...." And not much later as told in verse 19, "And out of the ground the Lord God formed every beast of the field, and every fowl of the air...." There are many other scriptural references to both ground and earth but when growing plants and living animals are being discussed, it is usually in terms of the ground, thus: "...cursed in the ground for thy sake..." (Genesis 3:17) and "...but Cain was a tiller of the ground...." (Genesis 4:2.)

Usage of the term ground emphasizes a basic unifying fact about the physical (not spiritual) origin of all earthly beings. Plants, animals, and even man are described as being made of one common material. And finally this sobering thought:

"In the sweat of thy face shalt thou eat bread, till thou return unto the ground; for out of it wast thou taken; for dust thou art, and unto dust shalt thou return."

Genesis 3:19

No other phraseology gives such perfect opportunity for a choice between the figurative and the literal. It might even be said that here one is forced to choose between the mystical earth-bound thinking of ancient times and the precise thinking of the scientific present. It was not difficult for men of ancient or medieval times to imagine the bringing forth of man as a magical or supernatural act. Artists represented the event time and time again as the instantaneous transformation of an inert and lifeless image of a man into a perfect, living person. Comparisons were based on common experience such as the shaping of vessels by the village potter. That God should do the shaping seems to be required by scriptural authority; God was the one who made man and animals. The most logical way to make anything is with ones hands.

"But now, O Lord, thou art our father; we are the clay,
and thou our potter; and we all are the work of thy hand."
Isaiah 65:8

The picture of God literally shaping man with his hands as a potter shapes his clay is beautiful and impressive imagery suitable and irreproachable for a more innocent age. But with the passage of time the image of the Great Potter has faded and other interpretations have emerged. Man is still seen as being made of the dust but in a more indirect and complicated way. How dust, ground, clay, or soil become living tissue is studied today in numerous technical fields including biochemistry, nutrition and physiology. And how to manage the dust of the earth so as to make it productive and keep our own allotment of clay alive has become a major problem of mankind.

Modern science has made clear the successive steps required in the conversion of the raw materials of the earth into muscle, eye and brain. Much of the magic has faded but the wonder is no less. And what has this modern knowledge done to the creation story? To some it has revealed the Genesis account as a fable made up by and for the superstitious and ignorant. Others, more tolerant of the seeming childishness of an earlier age, have substituted their own latter-day interpretation. The making of living things from the dust of the ground is no less significant to them than would be the infusion of life into a statue of stone. They see God not as a Great Potter but as a Great Chemist. To this group God must still be there, weighing and measuring as it were the proper combination of things to bring life and individuality to each of his numerous creations. Since each kind is different, each has its own recipe, its own formula, its own genetic code and its own time of creation. It is very special indeed, hence the idea of special creation. This is the way today's Creationists view it—they recognize a divine miracle while admitting most of the assertions of science. What they do demand is the immanent presence and agency of God in bringing forth all life. To them any other view is intolerable and irreverent.

Evolutionists, by contrast, believe that the power of shaping the individual and of producing the species lies in the genes. In the genes, they see in capsule form the accumulated outcome of ages of trial and error together with mechanisms for transmitting this vital information and of improving on it. This view obviously does not require the presence of God at the creation of every new kind of life. In fact it may not require his assistance even at the birth of the first life. Persons who follow this line of thinking are clearly at odds with traditional views of the creation and with contemporary creationism. Since evolutionists seem to have eliminated the necessity for God in creating the species they are accused of eliminating him altogether. This accusation is accepted without shame, guilt or remorse by many who would rather believe in no God at all than one who is impotent, ridiculous or unnecessary.

Many, if not most, informed persons brought up in the Judeo-Christian tradition find themselves caught between the extremes of creationism and evolutionism. These are in the main religious men and women who want to believe the Bible and will fight to defend it. To them the findings of science no matter how logical are dangerous and faith destroying. If the public polls are to be believed, the present is a time of return to the Bible. The greatest resurgence of belief is among the evangelical and fundamentalist sects many of which profess to accept scripture as literally true. It seems paradoxical that this return to the Bible comes at a time when space explorations and great discoveries in biology and geology make literal interpretations more difficult than ever before.

Obviously, millions of persons must be disregarding the problem while others may be striving secretly to make up their minds. The attitude that religion is in conflict with science and that science is wrong is fortified by many Christian ministers. Unfortunately these leaders seem to offer their followers only the alternatives of creationism or evolutionism. Scientists, in the main, appear unperturbed. To them the problem of the appearance and proliferation of species has been solved in favor of evolution. Any further argument is a waste of time; if the Bible conflicts with science it is the Bible that must give way. Certainly not to be overlooked are those dissident scientists who profess full belief in the scripture and do not go along with their colleagues on such subjects as the age of the earth and organic evolution. Some of these belong to the Creation Research Society, others may share the same views but are not formally affiliated with the Society.

There is one more group and it is the smallest of all. Its members profess to believe in God but do not wish to be called creationists in the sense that the term is currently applied. They have had to abandon traditional scriptural interpretations and are therefore regarded with hostility by their theological contemporaries and with a degree of distain by their scientific colleagues. Time will tell whether a place can be found for this minority.

Man and Animals

Man, in spite of his importance, did not have a day of creation that was exclusively his own. According to scripture he entered the scene on the sixth day preceded by other land-living animals in great variety. The relationship of men and animals has been a most puzzling one for thinkers throughout the ages. No matter what view one may have of the origin of man the presence of other beings that resemble him in various degrees is a fact to be dealt with in all seriousness.

In some societies animals are called brothers and treated accordingly. In fables beyond number the beasts are given the attributes of human speech, thought, and action. Animals have been variously worshipped as gods, regarded with fear and superstition, hunted to extinction, domesticated for food and kept as intimate pets or valued servants. Obviously they can be cast in no simple role.

It would be foolish to deny that in the pre-scientific ages man felt and made abundantly manifest a close kinship with the animals. In many societies the status of man was exactly that of an animal— he being different not so much in kind as in degree from his associates of the forests and plains. With the scientific age, zoology and comparative anatomy began to look at living things in objective ways with the conclusion that man is officially classed as an animal.

Furthermore he is a chordate (has a dorsal nervous system), vertebrate (a backbone), a mammal (hair, milk), a primate (5 fingers, 32 teeth, steroscopic vision) and finally a homonoid (large brain, erect posture, even row of teeth).

Although the zoological assignment of man among the animals seems well founded and unarguable, reactions to it have ranged from bitter outrage through weary resignation, to gladsome relief.

In spite of the fact that science places man in the highest category of the animal world this is not good enough for most of us.

We want a separate more exalted position. We shudder at the sight of what science declares to be our distant living relatives, the apes, and are repelled by the fossilized remains of the still closer kinfolk that scientists have disinterred from the earth. Many sternly disavow any relationship with the rest of creation and place heavy blame upon science for classifying man as an animal related to the monkeys. But a kinship is too obvious; man like the other animals, must eat to live, his body functions are disgustingly beastial, his methods of reproduction are no better than those of the monkeys, he is born in blood and water, he suffers, dies and decays like all flesh. In the face of all his earthly trappings how can he in good conscience place himself above the rest of the animal creation? In their more reflective moments some may wonder why God made man so much like the monkey or vice versa. Should not the crown of creation be something more special, more glorious, more god-like in its form and functions? Is the distinction no more than that implied by the title of a popular book, "The Naked Ape"?

What do scriptures have to say about the relationship of man and the other animals? Creationists are fond of pointing out that God *made* the beasts of the earth and cattle and creeping things but that he *created* man from the dust of the earth in his own image, inferring that\there could be no evolutionary connection between man and any lower creations. But the way is left open for such a connection and why it is neither specifically denied or affirmed must remain a matter of individual speculation.

Consider these similarities in the description of the coming forth of man and of animals:

(a) Both are made from the dust of the ground.

"And the Lord God formed man of the dust of the ground..."

Genesis 2:7

"And out of the ground the Lord God formed every beast of the field and every fowl of the air..."

Genesis 2:19

(b) Both received the breath of life from God.

"...and breathed into his (man's) nostrils the breath of life...."

Genesis 2:7

"...for I God, breathed into them (beasts and fowls) the breath of life..."

Moses 3:19

(c) Both became living souls.

"...and man became a living soul."

Genesis 2:7

"and they (beasts and fowls) were also living souls..."

Moses 3:19

(d) Both were to exist by the same means.

"...Behold, I have given you (man) every herb bearing seed...every tree...*to you it shall be for meat.*"

Genesis 1:29

"And to every beast of the earth, and every fowl of the air, and to every thing that creepeth upon the earth, wherein there is life, *I have given every green herb for meat...*"

Genesis 1:30

Where then is there a difference between man and animal that can be defended by the creation scripture? In the last analysis it is in his assigned status more than in his indicated origin that man is clearly given a position superior to animals. God did not exactly command man to assume dominion but the meaning is unmistakable: "and have dominion over the fish of the sea, and over the fowl of the air, and over every living thing that moveth upon the earth." (Genesis 1:28.) Later Adam gave names to the beasts of the field and fowl of the air, an act proving his superiority over them.

In proving something special in the nature of man we must evidently go beyond the creation scripture. By putting scattered bits of evidence together one learns that it is in the matter of his spirit that man is different. Not that animals do not have spirits while man does. The statement that animals became living souls would seem to require that they have spirits. Like man they have bodies and spirits but it is the nature of the spirit that makes a difference. Abraham is the most precise: "...the Gods formed man from the dust of the ground, and took his spirit (that is, the man's spirit), and put it into him...and man became a living soul." (Abraham 5:7.) This does not rule out the possibility that animals did not originate in the same way—the evident purpose of this scripture, especially the parenthetical insertion, is to make clear that it was man's and not God's spirit that was placed in man's body. But add this, "...I, the Lord God, had created all the children of men; and not yet a man to till the ground; for in heaven created I them; and there was not yet flesh upon the earth, neither in the water, neither in the air." (Moses 3:5.) Latter-day scripture makes clear that men are offspring of God—the children of a Heavenly Father. Each man and woman is an eternal personality. No such origin can be proven for animals. They are creations of God but not his offspring.

Theologians seem unable or unwilling to agree on a specific description of how man's physical body came into being. To say that it was miraculous or supernatural in this day of scientific inquiry is not enough. Science has at least provided a theory as to how physical man could have originated and is steadily accumulating evidence to support it. But theologians have mostly condemned the theory of organic evolution in such horrifying terms that the average Christian is convinced that it is not only erroneous but evil and dangerous.

As to the origin of the spirit of man things are even more uncertain. It is a subject on which science naturally is silent. Here, where theology might be expected to make one of its greatest contributions, there are deep-seated differences of opinion. The time, place and manner of creation of the spirit remain clouded in mystery.

It seems scarcely fair that science should be condemned for not proving a divine origin for the body of man when theology has trouble explaining the origin of the spirit. It is doubtful that science can do more than it has already done to dignify man. By any standard which measures success and eminence man is the crowning glory of creation. He has not only survived but has achieved dominance over all other living things. To zoologists man occupies the highest tip of the highest branch of the tree of life. He alone of living things makes up the species, genus and family to which he is assigned.

Theologians evidently want scientists to admit the possibility of a supernatural origin for man's body. On the other hand scientists are asking theologians to agree that a natural origin might be possible. That either side should give ground seems unlikely. Science has succeeded only when it has cast off any and all appeals to the supernatural. If theologians were to admit that man has evolved, they fear the danger of downgrading or eliminating God as the creator. Few on either side can perceive that evolution is a great creative process that dignifies man and glorifies God. Meanwhile, until reason prevails over pride and prejudice, the common man must struggle to reconcile his two opposing natures as best he can.

Comments and References

No one denies that man has been around for at least several thousand years. Some think he arrived fully developed at a relatively late date to take command of a world already prepared for him. Others say his roots go back billions of years and that he evolved along with the earth and other forms of life. Those who believe in his supernatural origin base their case chiefly on the Genesis account which states that man is a creation of God. What this phrase means is at the core of the argument between creationists and evolutionists.

It is not the purpose of this book to try to convince anyone that they should become either creationists or evolutionists. If a person has accepted the explanations offered for pre-human events he or she may be willing to abandon strict literal meanings and find naturalistic explanations not too objectionable. The literature on human origins is immense and has been written almost entirely by persons whose minds are already made up and who do not wish to contend over issues they consider to have been settled decades ago. Recent discussions of human origins are, I believe, more candid and less emotional than any previous time. The problem as seen by scientists is not, did man evolve, but rather how, where, and why did he evolve. A selection of recent titles such as given below illustrates the trend today: Ian Tattersall and Niles Eldridge, 1977, Fact, Theory, and Fantasy in Human Paleontology: *in* American Scientist, Vol. 65, no. 2; R. E. F. Leakey, 1976, Hominids in Africa: *in* American Scientist, Vol. 64, no. 2; Richard G. Klein, 1977, The Ecology of Early Man in Southern Africa: *in* Science, Vol. 197, no. 4299; Gina Bari Kolata, 1977, Human Evolution: *in* Science, Vol. 197, no. 4300; Henry M. McHenry, 1975, Fossils and the Mosaic Nature of Human Evolution: *in* Science, Vol. 190, no. 4213; David Pilbeam and S. J. Gould, 1974, Size and Scaling in Human Evolution: *in* Science, Vol. 186, no. 4167; Robert B. Eckhardt, 1972, Population Genetics and Human Origins, *in* Scientific American, Vol. 226, no. 1, Gina Bari Kolata, 1975, Human Evolution: Life-styles and Lineages of Early Hominids: *in* Science, Vol. 178, no. 4180; Laura Evans, 1972, Ancestral Secrets: *in* The Sciences, Vol. 12, no. 3.

References such as these might be multiplied endlessly and searched with scant solace by those who cannot accept evolutionary concepts. Practically nothing in present-day science writing will be found that argues against the evolution of man. But all sides deserve to be heard. The fact of growing opposition to evolution has been mentioned in reference to preceding chapters. A number of books, study guides, films, and newsletters are available from the Creation Research Society.

Latter-day Saints have produced their own anti-evolution literature and are encouraged to read it. Anti-evolution is certainly not a closed, restricted, or forbidden topic. Books that deal entirely or in part with evolution and anti-evolution by Latter-day Saint writers are: Joseph Fielding Smith, 1954, *Man—His Origin and Destiny,* Deseret Book Co.; Bruce R. McConkie, *Mormon Doctrine* (entry on evolution), 1958 and later editions, Bookcraft; Bruce R. McConkie (compiler), *Doctrines of Salvation,* Vol. 1 (discussions on evolution, creation, etc.), Bookcraft; Dean R. Zimmerman, 1976, *Evolution: A Golden Calf,* Hawkes Publishing, Inc.; Frank B. Salisbury, 1976, *The Creation,* Deseret Book Co.; Melvin A. Cook and Melvin G. Cook, 1968, *Science and Mormonism,* Deseret Book Co.

Every concerned reader will be faced with very serious problems as he or she studies these writings, especially those of highly respected authorities. Without trying to tell anyone what he or she should believe I make four simple suggestions: 1) Check cited references in their proper context and try to make an evaluation of the credibility and credentials of all sources; 2) Keep in mind the scriptural assurance that God created all men in heaven before they came to earth; 3) Know that on the subject of organic evolution the Church has officially taken no position, and; 4) Look for an answer to this basic question: Where and how did Adam obtain his physical body?

30

In Heaven Created I Them

"...And I, the Lord God, had created all the children of men; and not yet a man to till the ground; for in heaven created I them; and there was not yet flesh upon the earth, neither in the water, neither in the air;..."

Moses 3:5

Of the ante-mortal creation of man Genesis gives only a vague hint and Abraham little more. Moses by contrast is explicit. Whereas Genesis and Abraham suggest that vegetation existed "before it grew" Moses goes well beyond this to specify "all the children of men" as having had a pre-earth creation and existence. Furthermore, Heaven is designated as the place of man's previous experiences.

The location of the literal Heaven has already been discussed in chapter 16. There are more important problems relating to the history of man. How are the following concepts and scriptures to be reconciled?

a) Man was not created by God. (Scripture: "Man was also in the beginning with God." D&C 93:29.)

b) Man was created in Heaven. (Scripture: "...for in heaven created I them...." Moses 3:5.)

c) Man was created on earth. (Scripture: "And the Lord God formed man of the dust of the ground...." Genesis 2:7.)

That man is eternal is a basic belief of Latter-day Saints but theologians of other churches find the concept difficult to accept. Nevertheless the idea of an eternal God or an eternal Father is common to all Christian sects and to Judaism as well. The view that man is a creation of God and yet at the same time co-eternal with him is understandably confusing. The problem in a different guise was argued for centuries in the early churches: how could Christ, a mortal offspring and creation of God be equal with his father who made him? Nevertheless, "Man was also in the beginning with God. Intelligence, or the light of truth, was not created or made, neither indeed can be." (D&C 93:29.) Joseph Smith has elaborated on this topic and has this to say (Teachings of the Prophet Joseph Smith, p. 158): "The spirit of man is not a created being; it existed from eternity, and will exist to eternity. Anything created cannot be eternal; and earth, water, etc., had their existence in an elementary state, from eternity. Our Savior speaks of children and says, Their angels always stand before my Father. The Father called all spirits before Him at the creation of man, and organized them. He (Adam) is the head, and was told to multiply."

This is a difficult passage to reconcile with other scripture. An editorial footnote to a compilation of the teachings of the Prophet Joseph Smith provided by Joseph Fielding Smith (before he became President of the Church) states: "In saying the spirit of man is not created the Prophet without any doubt had in mind the intelligence as explained in the Doctrine and Covenants, Section 93:29: 'Man was also in the beginning with God. Intelligence, or the light of truth, was not created or made, neither indeed can be.' From this we gather that the intelligence in man was not created, but the Prophet taught very clearly that man is in very deed the offspring of God, and that the spirits of men were born in the spirit world the children of God. See Doctrine and Covenants 76:23." (Doctrine and Covenants 76:24, not 76:23, reads: "That by him, and through him, and of him, the worlds are and were created, and the inhabitants thereof are begotten sons and daughters unto God.") (W.L.S.)

This is not the place to discuss the mystery of the eternal intelligent essence of man. It is the fact of a dual or two-stage creation that is more important to the present topic. Only to those who know themselves to be personalities of body and of spirit is there no mystery. Likewise only to those who know the reality of a pre-existence are the scriptures clear and believable. Genesis, as stated, is not unmistakably precise as to the pre-mortal or spiritual creation of man. But neither is it entirely silent; Genesis 2:5 mentions "...every plant of the field before it was in the earth and every herb of the field before it grew." Moses is much more specific (somewhere, somehow a very vital part of the original words have been omitted). Moses 3:5 reads in part "...For I, the Lord God, created all things, of which I have spoken, spiritually, before they were naturally upon the face of the earth." We do not know the details of our spiritual birth and our pre-existence and for the time being must accept the parenthood of God and his role in bringing our spirits into existence as accomplished facts. Only by such acceptance does the thought of a previous creation cease to become a barrier to proper understanding of many scriptures, particularly those describing the creation.

Finally, we have God's word that man was indeed created (organized) on this earth. The familiar scriptural assertion that "...the Lord God formed man of the dust of the ground..." seems to admit of no other conclusion. But it was his physical body only that had this origin. That the body of the first man originated on earth is not disputed—it is the how and the when of the event that are subjects of bitter controversy. Perhaps those who are puzzled by the origin of man should consider if this is a matter about which something may be learned by scientific study and research or must it be made known only by divine revelation through ecclesiastical channels?

Comments and References

Of all the concepts that separate Mormonism from the rest of Christianity (and Judaism) few are more profound than beliefs regarding the origin of the human spirit. Latter-day Saints believe simply that men's spirits exist with God and are united with their physical bodies as a part of the birth process. "The body and the spirit are the soul of man." Other churches must struggle endlessly with the origin of the spirit or soul, because they reject the idea of a previous life. The Catholic dogma as I understand it is that the spirit is created at the moment of conception to take residence in the physical body with no previous existence or experience.

It might be said that Latter-day Saints beg the question by pushing back the origin of the individual to previous time. This is true—the idea that man is co-existent with God and at the same time his offspring is not easily comprehended. However, it is a concept that solves many problems about the relation of body and soul and requires an acceptance of the pre-existence of the human personality.

The simple six-word declaration of Moses 3:5 that every individual has been created in heaven by God is one of those enlightening statements that must have been in the original Genesis account.

Comments on the spirit or soul that seem to include all possible alternatives may be found in *The Catholic Encyclopedia*, Vol. IV, p. 476-477. The Latter-day Saint viewpoint is briefly described under the entry "Spirit Element" in *Mormon Doctrine*, a compilation by Bruce R. McConkie.

Index

St. Augustine, 16-17.
St. Thomas:
quoted, 18, 19; theologian 18.
Struggle to Survive, 162.
St. Vincent Millay, quoted, 30.
Sun:
angular momentum, 111; appearance
on third day, 80; becomes self-
luminous body, 112; celestial name is
Shinehah, 105; scriptural reference,
90; solar wind, 112-113; sunlight
essential to life, 125.
Sunlight:
essential to plant life, 124-125; solar
wind, 112-113.

T

Talmage, James E., quoted, 51, 185-186.
Tar Pits, fossils in, 154.
Temperature:
of nuclear reactions, 84, 112; relation
to states of water, 137; requirements
for life, 137-138; within stars, 83-84.
The Restoration, 23.
Thermonuclear Energy, 83-84, 90, 112.
Third Day: (of creation)
events of, 122-127; plants created or
organized, 123; sun and moon appear,
123-124.
Time, 174.

U

Universe:
age of, 49; expansion, 49; theories of
origin, 48-49.
Urim and Thummim:
place where God resides is a, 101;
used by Abraham, 100.

V

Van Loon, Hendrick W., 30.
Void:
descriptive of unorganized matter, 66;
scriptural and other meanings, 65-66.
Volcanoes:
around Pacific basin, 145; origin, 145;
relation to sea-floor spreading, 145;
source of ash and dust, 137.

W

Water:
absence on moon and mercury, 118;
in atmosphere, 180; escape from
earth, 181; essential to star formation,
79; face of, Genesis reference, 76-77;
to be filled with life, 161; gathered into
one place, 115; hydrological cycle,
138; of the hydrosphere, 146; importance to life, 137; on Mars, 144; meaning in scripture, 76; nature and
abundance, 137-144; necessity for in
development of the earth, 138; origin
of, 179-182; in protoplasm, 181; quantity on earth, 180; references, 182-183;
Ruby theory of origin, 180; scriptural
reference, 179; and sedimentary rocks,
181; several meanings, 115; in space,
77; states of in nature, 138; under the
firmament, 106; vapor on Jupiter, 125.
Watering: (of the earth)
important both scripturally and geologically, 182; first event of the seventh
day, 179, 182.
Wells, H. G., 30.

Y

Young, Brigham, quoted on eternity, 51.